5

Sequential Spelling

Student Workbook

conclude
conclusive
conclusion
intrude
intrusive
intrusion

ISBN: 9781935943150

Day 1

Spelling Lesson:

As you hear them, write the spelling words for the day in the space provided. Be sure that you correct any words you have spelled incorrectly.

1. _____

2. _____

3. _____

4. _____

5. _____

6. _____

7. _____

8. _____

9. _____

10. _____

11. _____

12. _____

13. _____

14. _____

15. _____

16. _____

17. _____

18. _____

19. _____

20. _____

21. _____

22. _____

23. _____

24. _____

25. _____

Using your Words:

List as many words as you can that have the following letters (in order) in them.

en

_____

_____

_____

_____

_____

_____

_____

_____

_____

Sequential Spelling Level 5 - Student Workbook

Day 2

Spelling Lesson:

As you hear them, write the spelling words for the day in the space provided. Be sure that you correct any words you have spelled incorrectly.

1. _____

2. _____

3. _____

4. _____

5. _____

6. _____

7. _____

8. _____

9. _____

10. _____

11. _____

12. _____

13. _____

14. _____

15. _____

16. _____

17. _____

18. _____

19. _____

20. _____

21. _____

22. _____

23. _____

24. _____

25. _____

Using your words:

Choose ten of today's spelling words and use them in a paragraph, silly story or poem.

_____

_____

_____

_____

_____

_____

_____

_____

_____

_____

Day 3

As you hear them, write the spelling words for the day in the space provided. Be sure that you correct any words you have spelled incorrectly.

1. _____

2. _____

3. _____

4. _____

5. _____

6. _____

7. _____

8. _____

9. _____

10. _____

11. _____

12. _____

13. _____

14. _____

15. _____

16. _____

17. _____

18. _____

19. _____

20. _____

21. _____

22. _____

23. _____

24. _____

25. _____

Using your Words:

Unscramble these:

1. refeerhns _____

2. sciehitzpin _____

3. etkson _____

4. aeeltina _____

5. vnare _____

6. hseparner _____

7. namets _____

8. grenaedd _____

9. tniemt _____

10. eehahnpyt _____

Day 4

Spelling Lesson:

As you hear them, write the spelling words for the day in the space provided. Be sure that you correct any words you have spelled incorrectly.

1. _____

2. _____

3. _____

4. _____

5. _____

6. _____

7. _____

8. _____

9. _____

10. _____

11. _____

12. _____

13. _____

14. _____

15. _____

16. _____

17. _____

18. _____

19. _____

20. _____

21. _____

22. _____

23. _____

24. _____

25. _____

Using your Words:

Can you find the words?

```
Q S H A R P E N E R S G L F Z R V O
D P C W E K M N Z R R A R F S K I S
E K I D I S A G U A O O M R Z K X D
A U R O D J D A Y V M S I E Q M E M
D K C Z K N D R Q E E S T S K S N H
E O U E F K E D N N N E T H N I S V
N Y I N J C N E P S S V E E V R P Y
I H T S O X I N S U E N N B E U P
N I S U X X N I G V W N S E Q N N I
G D G C E I G N S Z G T K R A S I X
P M H H N F D G R X M Y H S Y X O L
Z U P J E K P Q L G G I X U M D F Y
```

Find the following words in the puzzle.
Words are hidden → ↓ and ↘ .

CIRCUITS   MADDENING   SEVENTY
DEADENING   MITTENS   SHARPENERS
DOZENS   OMENS   SIRENS
FRESHENERS   OXEN   VIXENS
GARDENING   RAVENS

Day 5

As you hear them, write the spelling words for the day in the space provided. Be sure that you correct any words you have spelled incorrectly.

1. _____

2. _____

3. _____

4. _____

5. _____

6. _____

7. _____

8. _____

9. _____

10. _____

11. _____

12. _____

13. _____

14. _____

15. _____

16. _____

17. _____

18. _____

19. _____

20. _____

21. _____

22. _____

23. _____

24. _____

25. _____

Using your words:

Fill in the blanks with words from today's spelling list.

1. _____ the tea with honey.

2. My mom says I should _____.

3. When water freezes it will _____ to ice.

4. An engineer will _____ a new product.

5. It's time to _____ and get up!

6. Exercise will _____ your body.

7. I saw a _____ fly over our house.

8. I need a _____ to get the gas out of the tank.

9. Poor nutrition may _____ you.

10. We saw a _____ at the zoo!

Day 6

As you hear them, write the spelling words for the day in the space provided. Be sure that you correct any words you have spelled incorrectly.

1. _____

2. _____

3. _____

4. _____

5. _____

6. _____

7. _____

8. _____

9. _____

10. _____

11. _____

12. _____

13. _____

14. _____

15. _____

16. _____

17. _____

18. _____

19. _____

20. _____

21. _____

22. _____

23. _____

24. _____

25. _____

Using your words:

Choose ten of today's spelling words and use them in a paragraph, silly story or poem.

_____

_____

_____

_____

_____

_____

_____

_____

_____

_____

Day 7

Spelling Lesson:

As you hear them, write the spelling words for the day in the space provided. Be sure that you correct any words you have spelled incorrectly.

1. _____

2. _____

3. _____

4. _____

5. _____

6. _____

7. _____

8. _____

9. _____

10. _____

11. _____

12. _____

13. _____

14. _____

15. _____

16. _____

17. _____

18. _____

19. _____

20. _____

21. _____

22. _____

23. _____

24. _____

25. _____

Using your words:

Use a dictionary to find the meanings of the following words. Then use each of them correctly in a sentence.

1.awakened _____

_____

2.threatened _____

_____

3.frightened _____

_____

4.fastened _____

_____

5.designed _____

_____

6.resigned _____

_____

7.maligned _____

_____

8.signature _____

_____

9.beacon _____

_____

10.siphoned _____

_____

Day 8

Spelling Lesson:

As you hear them, write the spelling words for the day in the space provided. Be sure that you correct any words you have spelled incorrectly.

1. _____

2. _____

3. _____

4. _____

5. _____

6. _____

7. _____

8. _____

9. _____

10. _____

11. _____

12. _____

13. _____

14. _____

15. _____

16. _____

17. _____

18. _____

19. _____

20. _____

21. _____

22. _____

23. _____

24. _____

25. _____

Using your words:

Make as many words as you can from the following word.

strengthening

1._____

2._____

3._____

4._____

5._____

6._____

7._____

8._____

9._____

10._____

11._____

12._____

13._____

14._____

Sequential Spelling Level 5 - Student Workbook

Spelling Lesson:

As you hear them, write the spelling words for the day in the space provided. Be sure that you correct any words you have spelled incorrectly.

1. _____

2. _____

3. _____

4. _____

5. _____

6. _____

7. _____

8. _____

9. _____

10. _____

11. _____

12. _____

13. _____

14. _____

15. _____

16. _____

17. _____

18. _____

19. _____

20. _____

21. _____

22. _____

23. _____

24. _____

25. _____

Using your words:

Fill in the blanks with words from today's spelling list.

1. We like to _____ in the gym.

2. The river snakes through the _____.

3. Can I _____ my pawn two spaces?

4. Did you have a _____ to do the dishes?

5. "A _____ is a _____, no matter how small!"

6. Did you find this _____ easy?

7. The _____ runs the family of elephants.

8. They fired the _____ on the Fourth of July.

9. My brother likes to study _____.

10. We went to _____ on vacation.

Spelling Lesson:

As you hear them, write the spelling words for the day in the space provided. Be sure that you correct any words you have spelled incorrectly.

1. _____

2. _____

3. _____

4. _____

5. _____

6. _____

7. _____

8. _____

9. _____

10. _____

11. _____

12. _____

13. _____

14. _____

15. _____

16. _____

17. _____

18. _____

19. _____

20. _____

21. _____

22. _____

23. _____

24. _____

25. _____

Using your words:

Unscramble these:

1. drcnaes _____

2. csnvaaed _____

3. sosesnl _____

4. nacosn _____

5. osmsumn _____

6. cnsaper _____

7. sroanecm _____

8. ensosmr _____

9. annosyc _____

10. roamnts _____

Day 11

As you hear them, write the spelling words for the day in the space provided. Be sure that you correct any words you have spelled incorrectly.

1. _____

2. _____

3. _____

4. _____

5. _____

6. _____

7. _____

8. _____

9. _____

10. _____

11. _____

12. _____

13. _____

14. _____

15. _____

16. _____

17. _____

18. _____

19. _____

20. _____

21. _____

22. _____

23. _____

24. _____

25. _____

Using your words:

Choose ten of today's spelling words and use them in a paragraph, silly story or poem.

_____

_____

_____

_____

_____

_____

_____

_____

_____

Day 12

As you hear them, write the spelling words for the day in the space provided. Be sure that you correct any words you have spelled incorrectly.

1. _____

2. _____

3. _____

4. _____

5. _____

6. _____

7. _____

8. _____

9. _____

10. _____

11. _____

12. _____

13. _____

14. _____

15. _____

16. _____

17. _____

18. _____

19. _____

20. _____

21. _____

22. _____

23. _____

24. _____

25. _____

Using your words:

Can you find the words?

```
K  D  U  Z  N  L  C  Z  T  C  R  I  M  S  O  N  U  S
G  P  E  R  S  O  N  A  L  I  T  Y  J  N  R  R  H  U
L  I  L  X  Y  B  A  R  O  N  S  X  M  N  K  J  G  M
A  N  G  V  V  R  O  M  A  N  T  I  C  A  L  L  Y  M
N  R  S  O  L  O  M  O  N  V  I  D  Z  Y  T  Q  X  O
C  H  A  P  R  O  N  S  L  K  X  M  A  L  Y  L  D  N
I  U  V  N  D  R  Z  K  O  L  A  W  F  N  O  B  E  I
N  L  U  N  C  H  E  O  N  S  N  V  K  E  C  H  M  N
G  A  R  M  J  R  O  C  I  Z  T  U  L  Z  K  I  O  G
U  C  I  R  C  U  M  S  T  A  N  C  E  S  Q  L  N  S
F  I  N  A  N  C  I  A  L  L  Y  H  L  N  Q  R  S  G
A  W  H  E  Z  P  A  T  R  O  N  S  W  G  N  C  N  G
```

Find the following words in the puzzle.
Words are hidden → ↓ and ↘ .

APRONS   DEMONS   PERSONALITY
BARONS   FINANCIALLY   ROMANTICALLY
CIRCUMSTANCES   GLANCING   SOLOMON
CRIMSON   LUNCHEONS   SUMMONING
DANCING   PATRONS

Day 13

Spelling Lesson:

As you hear them, write the spelling words for the day in the space provided. Be sure that you correct any words you have spelled incorrectly.

1. _____

2. _____

3. _____

4. _____

5. _____

6. _____

7. _____

8. _____

9. _____

10. _____

11. _____

12. _____

13. _____

14. _____

15. _____

16. _____

17. _____

18. _____

19. _____

20. _____

21. _____

22. _____

23. _____

24. _____

25. _____

Using your words:

Fill in the blanks with words from today's spelling list.

1. To play sports you need _____.

2. There was an _____ of food at the party.

3. My car needs some very expensive _____.

4. The patriots decided to _____ British rule.

5. Would you like a _____ for breakfast?

6. They said _____ to the nosy neighbor.

7. Don't let him _____ you with his taunts.

8. Keep your _____ on the beam.

9. Your speech was _____! We loved it!

10. It was _____, too!

Day 14

Spelling Lesson:

As you hear them, write the spelling words for the day in the space provided. Be sure that you correct any words you have spelled incorrectly.

1. _____

2. _____

3. _____

4. _____

5. _____

6. _____

7. _____

8. _____

9. _____

10. _____

11. _____

12. _____

13. _____

14. _____

15. _____

16. _____

17. _____

18. _____

19. _____

20. _____

21. _____

22. _____

23. _____

24. _____

25. _____

Using your words:

Unscramble these:

1. lleexencce _____

2. iatsnnt _____

3. cienevol _____

4. densatci _____

5. acbsanle _____

6. ltetans _____

7. eyegcrn _____

8. yisnfgi _____

9. papyl _____

10. iqtcauenacan _____

Day 15

As you hear them, write the spelling words for the day in the space provided. Be sure that you correct any words you have spelled incorrectly.

1. _____

2. _____

3. _____

4. _____

5. _____

6. _____

7. _____

8. _____

9. _____

10. _____

11. _____

12. _____

13. _____

14. _____

15. _____

16. _____

17. _____

18. _____

19. _____

20. _____

21. _____

22. _____

23. _____

24. _____

25. _____

Using your words:

Make as many words as you can from the following word.

acquaintances

Day 16

Spelling Lesson:

As you hear them, write the spelling words for the day in the space provided. Be sure that you correct any words you have spelled incorrectly.

1. _____

2. _____

3. _____

4. _____

5. _____

6. _____

7. _____

8. _____

9. _____

10. _____

11. _____

12. _____

13. _____

14. _____

15. _____

16. _____

17. _____

18. _____

19. _____

20. _____

21. _____

22. _____

23. _____

24. _____

25. _____

Using your words:

Choose ten of today's spelling words and use them in a paragraph, silly story or poem.

Spelling Lesson:

As you hear them, write the spelling words for the day in the space provided. Be sure that you correct any words you have spelled incorrectly.

1. _____

2. _____

3. _____

4. _____

5. _____

6. _____

7. _____

8. _____

9. _____

10. _____

11. _____

12. _____

13. _____

14. _____

15. _____

16. _____

17. _____

18. _____

19. _____

20. _____

21. _____

22. _____

23. _____

24. _____

25. _____

Using your words:

Make as many words as you can with the following letters (in order) in them.

ent

_____

_____

_____

_____

_____

_____

_____

_____

_____

_____

Day 18

Spelling Lesson:

As you hear them, write the spelling words for the day in the space provided. Be sure that you correct any words you have spelled incorrectly.

1. _____

2. _____

3. _____

4. _____

5. _____

6. _____

7. _____

8. _____

9. _____

10. _____

11. _____

12. _____

13. _____

14. _____

15. _____

16. _____

17. _____

18. _____

19. _____

20. _____

21. _____

22. _____

23. _____

24. _____

25. _____

Using your words:

Fill in the blanks with words from today's spelling list:

1. Have less _____ ! Take your time!

2. You should always act with _____.

3. The news _____ told the story.

4. Some school boards have _____ while others have

   _____.

5. You should be _____ to mom and dad.

6. We were accused of _____ in the accident.

7. We recognized her _____ in her field of study.

8. The _____ knew much more than we thought.

9. _____ happen! Be careful!

10. We are all _____ at some point.

As you hear them, write the spelling words for the day in the space provided. Be sure that you correct any words you have spelled incorrectly.

1. _____

2. _____

3. _____

4. _____

5. _____

6. _____

7. _____

8. _____

9. _____

10. _____

11. _____

12. _____

13. _____

14. _____

15. _____

16. _____

17. _____

18. _____

19. _____

20. _____

21. _____

22. _____

23. _____

24. _____

25. _____

Using your words:

Unscramble these:

1. accnelaidt   _____

2. nipnnceddeee   _____

3. npuetimd   _____

4. ateprn   _____

5. apantpre   _____

6. erceofnenc   _____

7. ylietnved   _____

8. notntcein   _____

9. pcrineysed   _____

10. ideceenbo   _____

Day 20

Spelling Lesson:

As you hear them, write the spelling words for the day in the space provided. Be sure that you correct any words you have spelled incorrectly.

1. _____

2. _____

3. _____

4. _____

5. _____

6. _____

7. _____

8. _____

9. _____

10. _____

11. _____

12. _____

13. _____

14. _____

15. _____

16. _____

17. _____

18. _____

19. _____

20. _____

21. _____

22. _____

23. _____

24. _____

25. _____

Using Your Words:

Make as many words as you can from the following word.

correspondence

Day 21

As you hear them, write the spelling words for the day in the space provided. Be sure that you correct any words you have spelled incorrectly.

1. _____

2. _____

3. _____

4. _____

5. _____

6. _____

7. _____

8. _____

9. _____

10. _____

11. _____

12. _____

13. _____

14. _____

15. _____

16. _____

17. _____

18. _____

19. _____

20. _____

21. _____

22. _____

23. _____

24. _____

25. _____

Using your words:

Choose ten of today's spelling words and use them in a paragraph, silly story or poem.

_____

_____

_____

_____

_____

_____

_____

_____

_____

Day 22

Spelling Lesson:

As you hear them, write the spelling words for the day in the space provided. Be sure that you correct any words you have spelled incorrectly.

1. _____

2. _____

3. _____

4. _____

5. _____

6. _____

7. _____

8. _____

9. _____

10. _____

11. _____

12. _____

13. _____

14. _____

15. _____

16. _____

17. _____

18. _____

19. _____

20. _____

21. _____

22. _____

23. _____

24. _____

25. _____

Using your words:

Use each of these words correctly in a sentence.

1. competently_____

_____

2. potency_____

_____

3. existent_____

_____

4. persistent_____

_____

5. minces_____

_____

6. ounces_____

_____

7. flounces_____

_____

8. trounces_____

_____

9. pronounces_____

_____

10. denounces_____

_____

Spelling Lesson:

As you hear them, write the spelling words for the day in the space provided. Be sure that you correct any words you have spelled incorrectly.

1. _____

2. _____

3. _____

4. _____

5. _____

6. _____

7. _____

8. _____

9. _____

10. _____

11. _____

12. _____

13. _____

14. _____

15. _____

16. _____

17. _____

18. _____

19. _____

20. _____

21. _____

22. _____

23. _____

24. _____

25. _____

Using Your Words:

Choose ten of the words in your spelling list and use each word in a sentence.

1._____

_____

2._____

_____

3._____

_____

4._____

_____

5._____

_____

6._____

_____

7._____

_____

8._____

_____

9._____

_____

10._____

_____

Day 24

Spelling Lesson:

As you hear them, write the spelling words for the day in the space provided. Be sure that you correct any words you have spelled incorrectly.

1. _____

2. _____

3. _____

4. _____

5. _____

6. _____

7. _____

8. _____

9. _____

10. _____

11. _____

12. _____

13. _____

14. _____

15. _____

16. _____

17. _____

18. _____

19. _____

20. _____

21. _____

22. _____

23. _____

24. _____

25. _____

Using Your Words:

Unscramble these:

1. cereefners   _____

2. ccemypneot _____

3. fflecuean   _____

4. mncniig   _____

5. cneo   _____

6. innguboc   _____

7. encabes   _____

8. nuliftlniae   _____

9. inyatltople   _____

10. ienettsaporn _____

Day 25

As you hear them, write the spelling words for the day in the space provided. Be sure that you correct any words you have spelled incorrectly.

1. _____

2. _____

3. _____

4. _____

5. _____

6. _____

7. _____

8. _____

9. _____

10. _____

11. _____

12. _____

13. _____

14. _____

15. _____

16. _____

17. _____

18. _____

19. _____

20. _____

21. _____

22. _____

23. _____

24. _____

25. _____

Using Your Words:

Fill in the blanks with words from today's spelling list.

1. My mom has a _____ bracelet.

2. Do you often _____ life?

3. We fish in our _____ .

4. The woods used to be full of _____ and thieves.

5. We marked the _____ of our property with stones.

6. Does this _____ to your understanding?

7. I am _____ of ice cream.

8. Will you _____ to my question, please?

9. It's a _____ ancient people built such a high _____ .

10. My word is my _____ .

Spelling Lesson:

As you hear them, write the spelling words for the day in the space provided. Be sure that you correct any words you have spelled incorrectly.

1. _____

2. _____

3. _____

4. _____

5. _____

6. _____

7. _____

8. _____

9. _____

10. _____

11. _____

12. _____

13. _____

14. _____

15. _____

16. _____

17. _____

18. _____

19. _____

20. _____

21. _____

22. _____

23. _____

24. _____

25. _____

Using Your Words:

Unscramble these:

1. dasbshun _____

2. nrerdsa _____

3. psond _____

4. densowr _____

5. soenrpd _____

6. sucponmdo _____

7. rpoecdrsons _____

8. nbdos _____

9. hndsuo _____

10. susdanto _____

Day 27

As you hear them, write the spelling words for the day in the space provided. Be sure that you correct any words you have spelled incorrectly.

1. _____

2. _____

3. _____

4. _____

5. _____

6. _____

7. _____

8. _____

9. _____

10. _____

11. _____

12. _____

13. _____

14. _____

15. _____

16. _____

17. _____

18. _____

19. _____

20. _____

21. _____

22. _____

23. _____

24. _____

25. _____

Using Your Words:

List as many words as you can with the following letters (in order) in them:

ound

Spelling Lesson:

As you hear them, write the spelling words for the day in the space provided. Be sure that you correct any words you have spelled incorrectly.

1. _____

2. _____

3. _____

4. _____

5. _____

6. _____

7. _____

8. _____

9. _____

10. _____

11. _____

12. _____

13. _____

14. _____

15. _____

16. _____

17. _____

18. _____

19. _____

20. _____

21. _____

22. _____

23. _____

24. _____

25. _____

Using your words:

Can you (find) the words?

```
R  U  K  H  O  U  N  D  I  N  G  I  W  S  Q  Y  U  K
W  K  Q  R  E  S  P  O  N  D  I  N  G  K  N  X  Q  Y
N  P  Z  W  Q  X  T  H  O  U  S  A  N  D  S  F  D  L
C  O  R  R  E  S  P  O  N  D  I  N  G  V  S  Z  Z  S
W  U  P  P  Y  Q  T  V  Z  V  Y  G  P  Y  X  F  T  I
A  N  O  T  N  Y  B  I  S  R  O  U  N  D  I  N  G  S
G  D  L  F  S  R  V  F  F  S  O  U  N  D  I  N  G  L
D  I  A  J  V  L  A  F  W  O  N  D  E  R  F  U  L  A
T  N  N  C  I  R  C  U  I  T  R  Y  Q  Z  X  V  G  N
N  G  D  J  D  Y  F  W  S  C  O  T  L  A  N  D  J  D
B  O  U  N  D  I  N  G  U  I  Q  S  T  U  F  R  N  S
G  L  S  G  R  O  U  N  D  I  N  G  O  S  V  B  W  Y
```

Find the following words in the puzzle.
Words are hidden → ↓ and ↘ .

BOUNDING
CIRCUITRY
CORRESPONDING
GROUNDING
HOUNDING

ISLANDS
POLAND
POUNDING
RESPONDING
ROUNDING

SCOTLAND
SOUNDING
THOUSANDS
WONDERFUL

Spelling Lesson:

As you hear them, write the spelling words for the day in the space provided. Be sure that you correct any words you have spelled incorrectly.

1. _____

2. _____

3. _____

4. _____

5. _____

6. _____

7. _____

8. _____

9. _____

10. _____

11. _____

12. _____

13. _____

14. _____

15. _____

16. _____

17. _____

18. _____

19. _____

20. _____

21. _____

22. _____

23. _____

24. _____

25. _____

Using your words:

Fill in the blanks with words from today's spelling list.

1. The mystery is such to _____ investigation.

2. We wrapped the packages in _____.

3. They use a _____ to load ships.

4. We need to _____ an emergency meeting!

5. The rooftop _____ pointed south.

6. Who is the _____ of Rome?

7. We went fishing for _____ in the ocean.

8. The strange outcome served to _____ us.

9. You should always be _____ to animals.

10. It's not _____. It's very routine.

Day 30

Spelling Lesson:

As you hear them, write the spelling words for the day in the space provided. Be sure that you correct any words you have spelled incorrectly.

1. _____

2. _____

3. _____

4. _____

5. _____

6. _____

7. _____

8. _____

9. _____

10. _____

11. _____

12. _____

13. _____

14. _____

15. _____

16. _____

17. _____

18. _____

19. _____

20. _____

21. _____

22. _____

23. _____

24. _____

25. _____

Using Your Words:

List as many words as you can with the following letters (in order) in them

ane

_____

_____

_____

_____

_____

_____

_____

_____

_____

_____

_____

_____

_____

Sequential Spelling Level 5 - Student Workbook

Day 31

As you hear them, write the spelling words for the day in the space provided. Be sure that you correct any words you have spelled incorrectly.

1. _____

2. _____

3. _____

4. _____

5. _____

6. _____

7. _____

8. _____

9. _____

10. _____

11. _____

12. _____

13. _____

14. _____

15. _____

16. _____

17. _____

18. _____

19. _____

20. _____

21. _____

22. _____

23. _____

24. _____

25. _____

Using Your Words:

Unscramble these:

1. uddfnoe   _____

2. nuedogrr   _____

3. nlpeiara   _____

4. syinta   _____

5. cednar   _____

6. naudenm   _____

7. noceoddufn   _____

8. nerseyc   _____

9. yivtan   _____

10. hrnaruiec   _____

Day 32

As you hear them, write the spelling words for the day in the space provided. Be sure that you correct any words you have spelled incorrectly.

1. _____

2. _____

3. _____

4. _____

5. _____

6. _____

7. _____

8. _____

9. _____

10. _____

11. _____

12. _____

13. _____

14. _____

15. _____

16. _____

17. _____

18. _____

19. _____

20. _____

21. _____

22. _____

23. _____

24. _____

25. _____

Using Your Words:

Choose ten words from your spelling list and use each of them in a sentence.

1._____

_____

2._____

_____

3._____

_____

4._____

_____

5._____

_____

6._____

_____

7._____

_____

8._____

_____

9._____

_____

10._____

_____

Day 33

As you hear them, write the spelling words for the day in the space provided. Be sure that you correct any words you have spelled incorrectly.

1. _____

2. _____

3. _____

4. _____

5. _____

6. _____

7. _____

8. _____

9. _____

10. _____

11. _____

12. _____

13. _____

14. _____

15. _____

16. _____

17. _____

18. _____

19. _____

20. _____

21. _____

22. _____

23. _____

24. _____

25. _____

Using Your Words:

List as many words as you can with the following letters (in order) in them

ine

Day 34

Spelling Lesson:

As you hear them, write the spelling words for the day in the space provided. Be sure that you correct any words you have spelled incorrectly.

1. _____

2. _____

3. _____

4. _____

5. _____

6. _____

7. _____

8. _____

9. _____

10. _____

11. _____

12. _____

13. _____

14. _____

15. _____

16. _____

17. _____

18. _____

19. _____

20. _____

21. _____

22. _____

23. _____

24. _____

25. _____

Using Your Words:

Fill in the blanks with words from today's spelling list.

1. _____ are soldiers in the navy.

2. There were lots of _____ in the ocean.

3. They put the sick in _____ to protect the rest of us.

4. On chemical element is called _____.

5. _____ are fun to jump on.

6. We all took _____ home from the airport.

7. There are _____ in the woods in Michigan.

8. We use _____ to help do work.

9. We all need _____ in our lives

10. My sister _____ stuff all the time.

Day 35

Spelling Lesson:

As you hear them, write the spelling words for the day in the space provided. Be sure that you correct any words you have spelled incorrectly.

1. _____

2. _____

3. _____

4. _____

5. _____

6. _____

7. _____

8. _____

9. _____

10. _____

11. _____

12. _____

13. _____

14. _____

15. _____

16. _____

17. _____

18. _____

19. _____

20. _____

21. _____

22. _____

23. _____

24. _____

25. _____

Using Your Words:

Unscramble these:

1. nvocneed   _____

2. icamnihts   _____

3. tnileas   _____

4. zmeaneniz   _____

5. gennesi   _____

6. ediiregtnnm   _____

7. ciernnaet   _____

8. rnevai   _____

9. irhacescna   _____

10. licenmaid   _____

Sequential Spelling Level 5 - Student Workbook

Day 36

As you hear them, write the spelling words for the day in the space provided. Be sure that you correct any words you have spelled incorrectly.

1. _____

2. _____

3. _____

4. _____

5. _____

6. _____

7. _____

8. _____

9. _____

10. _____

11. _____

12. _____

13. _____

14. _____

15. _____

16. _____

17. _____

18. _____

19. _____

20. _____

21. _____

22. _____

23. _____

24. _____

25. _____

Using Your Words:

Make as many words as you can from the following word.

predestination

Day 37

Spelling Lesson:

As you hear them, write the spelling words for the day in the space provided. Be sure that you correct any words you have spelled incorrectly.

1. _____

2. _____

3. _____

4. _____

5. _____

6. _____

7. _____

8. _____

9. _____

10. _____

11. _____

12. _____

13. _____

14. _____

15. _____

16. _____

17. _____

18. _____

19. _____

20. _____

21. _____

22. _____

23. _____

24. _____

25. _____

Using Your Words:

Fill in the blanks with words from today's spelling list.

1. I find this task a _____.

2. Jake showed _____ by his hard work.

3. The man made _____ in the Army.

4. We like _____ on our long sleeves.

5. I need a cough _____ for my throat.

6. The fire will _____ your hair.

7. What is the _____ of a religion?

8. Some languages have _____ and _____ words.

9. The flower _____ was beautiful.

10. We must _____ hatred from our hearts.

Spelling Lesson:

As you hear them, write the spelling words for the day in the space provided. Be sure that you correct any words you have spelled incorrectly.

1. _____

2. _____

3. _____

4. _____

5. _____

6. _____

7. _____

8. _____

9. _____

10. _____

11. _____

12. _____

13. _____

14. _____

15. _____

16. _____

17. _____

18. _____

19. _____

20. _____

21. _____

22. _____

23. _____

24. _____

25. _____

Using Your Words:

List as many words as you can that have these letters (in order).

eng; ung; inge

_____

_____

_____

_____

_____

_____

_____

_____

_____

_____

_____

_____

_____

_____

_____

Day 39

Spelling Lesson:

As you hear them, write the spelling words for the day in the space provided. Be sure that you correct any words you have spelled incorrectly.

1. _____

2. _____

3. _____

4. _____

5. _____

6. _____

7. _____

8. _____

9. _____

10. _____

11. _____

12. _____

13. _____

14. _____

15. _____

16. _____

17. _____

18. _____

19. _____

20. _____

21. _____

22. _____

23. _____

24. _____

25. _____

Using Your Words:

Can you  the words?

```
K  S  P  I  D  C  V  C  R  I  N  O  L  I  N  E  P  V
R  Y  C  N  I  N  L  H  S  P  L  U  N  G  E  D  T  A
A  R  R  D  B  Z  R  Q  Z  G  N  U  Y  K  B  J  Z  G
Y  I  I  O  W  R  B  X  R  V  M  P  N  A  F  F  P  H
M  N  N  C  T  R  E  V  E  N  G  E  D  G  N  V  A  E
M  G  G  T  F  N  D  E  I  L  L  N  V  T  E  Y  V  T
I  E  E  R  W  H  I  N  G  E  D  X  W  K  F  D  E  T
C  M  D  I  L  J  U  I  N  F  R  I  N  G  E  D  N  O
F  R  I  N  G  E  D  Y  X  M  R  L  D  D  W  I  G  P
K  O  D  A  H  P  A  G  E  A  N  T  R  Y  I  J  E  U
T  T  H  T  D  I  S  C  I  P  L  I  N  E  D  P  R  L
R  G  F  E  J  C  R  E  J  V  U  A  I  Z  P  H  B  N
```

Find the following words in the puzzle.
Words are hidden → ↓ and ↘ .

AVENGER   GHETTO   PAGEANTRY
CRINGED   HINGED   PLUNGED
CRINOLINE   INDOCTRINATE   REVENGED
DISCIPLINED   INFRINGED   SYRINGE
FRINGED   LUNGED

Spelling Lesson:

As you hear them, write the spelling words for the day in the space provided. Be sure that you correct any words you have spelled incorrectly.

1. _____

2. _____

3. _____

4. _____

5. _____

6. _____

7. _____

8. _____

9. _____

10. _____

11. _____

12. _____

13. _____

14. _____

15. _____

16. _____

17. _____

18. _____

19. _____

20. _____

21. _____

22. _____

23. _____

24. _____

25. _____

Using your words:

Choose ten of today's spelling words and use them in a paragraph, poem or silly story.

Name_____   Date_____

Evaluation Test #1

Fill in the blanks with the missing letters.

1. If you can't take the heat, stay out of the k_____.

2. Where's the pencil sh_____?

3. What's h_____?

4. I don't like to be thr_____.

5. I hope you're l_____ carefully.

6. The excuse was s_____:"my mother."

7. The doctor's s_____ was impossible to read.

8. Pers_____, I don't believe you.

9. You have a very fascinating pers_____.

10. Do you like to go d_____?

11. Do you think a full moon is rom_____?

12. It is very imp_____ for you to learn to spell.

13. Confid_____, I think you're catching on fast.

14. I have a friend who works at a conv_____ store.

15. My friend is very influ_____.

16. We were surr_____ by a hundred angry caterpillars.

17. I do not appreciate hearing prof_____.

18. Did you pass your physical exam_____?

19. Make sure you take your med_____.

20. Did you think this test was chall_____?

Day 41

Spelling Lesson:

As you hear them, write the spelling words for the day in the space provided. Be sure that you correct any words you have spelled incorrectly.

1. _____

2. _____

3. _____

4. _____

5. _____

6. _____

7. _____

8. _____

9. _____

10. _____

11. _____

12. _____

13. _____

14. _____

15. _____

16. _____

17. _____

18. _____

19. _____

20. _____

21. _____

22. _____

23. _____

24. _____

25. _____

Using Your Words:

Fill in the blanks with words from today's spelling list.

1. When a ship's crew rebels, it's a _____.

2. The _____ will dry in a day or two.

3. Shall we go for a _____?

4. We stood and looked out from the _____.

5. Are you angry? Do you have a _____.?

6. We waited in the _____ before takeoff.

7. I am feeling _____! Catch me!

8. That sound will _____ me forever.

9. We will need to _____ up a replacement.

10. That's _____ . It looks old-fashioned.

Day 42

As you hear them, write the spelling words for the day in the space provided. Be sure that you correct any words you have spelled incorrectly.

1. _____

2. _____

3. _____

4. _____

5. _____

6. _____

7. _____

8. _____

9. _____

10. _____

11. _____

12. _____

13. _____

14. _____

15. _____

16. _____

17. _____

18. _____

19. _____

20. _____

21. _____

22. _____

23. _____

24. _____

25. _____

Using your words:

Choose ten of today's spelling words and use them in a paragraph, silly story or poem.

_____

_____

_____

_____

_____

_____

_____

_____

_____

_____

Day 43

Spelling Lesson:

As you hear them, write the spelling words for the day in the space provided. Be sure that you correct any words you have spelled incorrectly.

1. _____

2. _____

3. _____

4. _____

5. _____

6. _____

7. _____

8. _____

9. _____

10. _____

11. _____

12. _____

13. _____

14. _____

15. _____

16. _____

17. _____

18. _____

19. _____

20. _____

21. _____

22. _____

23. _____

24. _____

25. _____

Using your words:

List as many words as you can that have the following letters (in order) in them.

aunt; aint

Spelling Lesson:

As you hear them, write the spelling words for the day in the space provided. Be sure that you correct any words you have spelled incorrectly.

1. _____

2. _____

3. _____

4. _____

5. _____

6. _____

7. _____

8. _____

9. _____

10. _____

11. _____

12. _____

13. _____

14. _____

15. _____

16. _____

17. _____

18. _____

19. _____

20. _____

21. _____

22. _____

23. _____

24. _____

25. _____

Using your words:

Choose ten of the words in your spelling list and use each word in a sentence.

1._____

_____

2._____

_____

3._____

_____

4._____

_____

5._____

_____

6._____

_____

7._____

_____

8._____

_____

9._____

_____

10._____

_____

Sequential Spelling Level 5 - Student Workbook

Day 45

Spelling Lesson:

As you hear them, write the spelling words for the day in the space provided. Be sure that you correct any words you have spelled incorrectly.

1. _____

2. _____

3. _____

4. _____

5. _____

6. _____

7. _____

8. _____

9. _____

10. _____

11. _____

12. _____

13. _____

14. _____

15. _____

16. _____

17. _____

18. _____

19. _____

20. _____

21. _____

22. _____

23. _____

24. _____

25. _____

Using your Words:

Fill in the blanks with words from today's spelling list.

1. Use some _____ to put it back together.

2. Be careful of _____ ivy in the woods.

3. Batman wears a _____.

4. A scout performs _____ for the army.

5. That move was quite _____.

6. Have you ever seen the _____ in the zoo?

7. What _____ is an orange?

8. Did you hear that _____?

9. We must _____ the _____ over the bar.

10. The _____ was littered with trash.

Day 46

Spelling Lesson:

As you hear them, write the spelling words for the day in the space provided. Be sure that you correct any words you have spelled incorrectly.

1. _____

2. _____

3. _____

4. _____

5. _____

6. _____

7. _____

8. _____

9. _____

10. _____

11. _____

12. _____

13. _____

14. _____

15. _____

16. _____

17. _____

18. _____

19. _____

20. _____

21. _____

22. _____

23. _____

24. _____

25. _____

Using your words:

Make as many words as you can with the following letters (in order) in them.

ape

Day 47

As you hear them, write the spelling words for the day in the space provided. Be sure that you correct any words you have spelled incorrectly.

1. _____

2. _____

3. _____

4. _____

5. _____

6. _____

7. _____

8. _____

9. _____

10. _____

11. _____

12. _____

13. _____

14. _____

15. _____

16. _____

17. _____

18. _____

19. _____

20. _____

21. _____

22. _____

23. _____

24. _____

25. _____

Using your words:

Unscramble these:

1. niosy   _____

2. osidnepo   _____

3. iuotsq   _____

4. aplceradns   _____

5. edepasc   _____

6. ahdspe   _____

7. pecra   _____

8. sanrewppe   _____

9. iexledpot   _____

10. degpa   _____

Spelling Lesson:

As you hear them, write the spelling words for the day in the space provided. Be sure that you correct any words you have spelled incorrectly.

1. _____

2. _____

3. _____

4. _____

5. _____

6. _____

7. _____

8. _____

9. _____

10. _____

11. _____

12. _____

13. _____

14. _____

15. _____

16. _____

17. _____

18. _____

19. _____

20. _____

21. _____

22. _____

23. _____

24. _____

25. _____

Using your words:

Choose ten of today's spelling words and use them in a paragraph, silly story or poem.

_____

_____

_____

_____

_____

_____

_____

_____

_____

_____

Spelling Lesson:

As you hear them, write the spelling words for the day in the space provided. Be sure that you correct any words you have spelled incorrectly.

1. _____

2. _____

3. _____

4. _____

5. _____

6. _____

7. _____

8. _____

9. _____

10. _____

11. _____

12. _____

13. _____

14. _____

15. _____

16. _____

17. _____

18. _____

19. _____

20. _____

21. _____

22. _____

23. _____

24. _____

25. _____

Using Your Words:

List as many words as you can that have the following letters (in order) in them.

aple

_____

_____

_____

_____

_____

_____

_____

_____

_____

_____

_____

_____

_____

_____

_____

_____

_____

_____

Sequential Spelling Level 5 - Student Workbook

Day 50

Spelling Lesson:

As you hear them, write the spelling words for the day in the space provided. Be sure that you correct any words you have spelled incorrectly.

1. _____

2. _____

3. _____

4. _____

5. _____

6. _____

7. _____

8. _____

9. _____

10. _____

11. _____

12. _____

13. _____

14. _____

15. _____

16. _____

17. _____

18. _____

19. _____

20. _____

21. _____

22. _____

23. _____

24. _____

25. _____

Using Your Words:

Unscramble these:

1. plstase _____

2. elsbrpuy _____

3. aicsnhapd _____

4. alpss _____

5. lpafs _____

6. spcsra _____

7. hcspa _____

8. gettho _____

9. asrpw _____

10. crupless _____

Day 51

As you hear them, write the spelling words for the day in the space provided. Be sure that you correct any words you have spelled incorrectly.

1. _____

2. _____

3. _____

4. _____

5. _____

6. _____

7. _____

8. _____

9. _____

10. _____

11. _____

12. _____

13. _____

14. _____

15. _____

16. _____

17. _____

18. _____

19. _____

20. _____

21. _____

22. _____

23. _____

24. _____

25. _____

Using Your Words:

Fill in the blanks with words from today's spelling list.

1. We borrowed a _____ at school.

2. The shutter broke loose and _____ in the breeze.

3. My mom and I _____ all afternoon.

4. The tree bent in the wind and then _____.

5. _____ people try to defraud others.

6. My lips are _____ from the wind.

7. The conman _____ the elderly couple.

8. All this running _____ our energy.

9. The swimmer _____ his opponents.

10. The sandwiches were _____ in foil.

Day 52

Spelling Lesson:

As you hear them, write the spelling words for the day in the space provided. Be sure that you correct any words you have spelled incorrectly.

1. _____

2. _____

3. _____

4. _____

5. _____

6. _____

7. _____

8. _____

9. _____

10. _____

11. _____

12. _____

13. _____

14. _____

15. _____

16. _____

17. _____

18. _____

19. _____

20. _____

21. _____

22. _____

23. _____

24. _____

25. _____

Using your words:

Can you  the words?

```
G W O H B V L F W C F N I P Z W D T
W Q R Y A E R Q S P K Y A X F Y E R
V K S A R N W G X T B F R B D T G A
E L S P P C D S T R A P P I N G D P
D A E L A P L I O A J P Y V Q P C P
U P P T A G I A C R P Z L U U M A E
P P Q S N P H N P A E P M E N N P R
I I V I K W P E G P P O I X R R P S
N N I E O M I I T U I P K N O S I B
G G W N J K D Q N T J N I K G P N R
Q U S N A P P I N G I H G N G H G L
C H A P P I N G Y X A G G X G N M Q
```

Find the following words in the puzzle.
Words are hidden → ↓ and ↘ .

CAPPING	LAPPING	STRAPPING
CHAPPING	SLAPPING	TAPPING
CLAPPING	SNAPPING	TRAPPERS
DUPING	SPAGHETTI	WRAPPING
HANDICAPPING	STAPLERS	

Sequential Spelling Level 5 - Student Workbook

Day 53

As you hear them, write the spelling words for the day in the space provided. Be sure that you correct any words you have spelled incorrectly.

1. _____

2. _____

3. _____

4. _____

5. _____

6. _____

7. _____

8. _____

9. _____

10. _____

11. _____

12. _____

13. _____

14. _____

15. _____

16. _____

17. _____

18. _____

19. _____

20. _____

21. _____

22. _____

23. _____

24. _____

25. _____

Using Your Words:

Fill in the blanks with words from today's spelling list.

1. How much does an _____ cost?

2. I have a new _____ with long ears.

3. We met in the _____ for services.

4. We need a _____ for the baby's bottle.

5. The sea is very _____ today.

6. We must _____ and _____ the door constantly

   for our dog.

7. _____ with your problems and solve them!

8. Did you hit a _____ in the baseball game?

9. What will _____ if we don't study?

10. The pebble sent out a _____ on the pond.

Day 54

As you hear them, write the spelling words for the day in the space provided. Be sure that you correct any words you have spelled incorrectly.

1. _____

2. _____

3. _____

4. _____

5. _____

6. _____

7. _____

8. _____

9. _____

10. _____

11. _____

12. _____

13. _____

14. _____

15. _____

16. _____

17. _____

18. _____

19. _____

20. _____

21. _____

22. _____

23. _____

24. _____

25. _____

Using Your Words:

Make as many words as you can from the following word.

grapples

Day 55

As you hear them, write the spelling words for the day in the space provided. Be sure that you correct any words you have spelled incorrectly.

1. _____

2. _____

3. _____

4. _____

5. _____

6. _____

7. _____

8. _____

9. _____

10. _____

11. _____

12. _____

13. _____

14. _____

15. _____

16. _____

17. _____

18. _____

19. _____

20. _____

21. _____

22. _____

23. _____

24. _____

25. _____

Using your words:

Choose ten of today's spelling words and use them in a paragraph, silly story or poem.

_____

_____

_____

_____

_____

_____

_____

_____

_____

_____

Day 56

Spelling Lesson:

As you hear them, write the spelling words for the day in the space provided. Be sure that you correct any words you have spelled incorrectly.

1. _____

2. _____

3. _____

4. _____

5. _____

6. _____

7. _____

8. _____

9. _____

10. _____

11. _____

12. _____

13. _____

14. _____

15. _____

16. _____

17. _____

18. _____

19. _____

20. _____

21. _____

22. _____

23. _____

24. _____

25. _____

Using your words:

Choose ten words from your spelling list and use each of them correctly in a sentence.

1._____

_____

2._____

_____

3._____

_____

4._____

_____

5._____

_____

6._____

_____

7._____

_____

8._____

_____

9._____

_____

10._____

_____

Sequential Spelling Level 5 - Student Workbook

Day 57

Spelling Lesson:

As you hear them, write the spelling words for the day in the space provided. Be sure that you correct any words you have spelled incorrectly.

1. _____

2. _____

3. _____

4. _____

5. _____

6. _____

7. _____

8. _____

9. _____

10. _____

11. _____

12. _____

13. _____

14. _____

15. _____

16. _____

17. _____

18. _____

19. _____

20. _____

21. _____

22. _____

23. _____

24. _____

25. _____

Using your words:

Fill in the blanks with words from today's spelling list.

1. _____ faces are comforting to see.

2. Is that man a Rhodes _____?

3. It will take a while to _____ the dog.

4. We need a more _____ response to this problem.

5. We need a _____ wrench, not a socket.

6. The mink is one _____ little creature.

7. Would you like _____ for your tea?

8. The chest is made of _____ wood.

9. A _____ is often a _____ , too!

10. There was a _____ of activity on the dock.

Day 58

As you hear them, write the spelling words for the day in the space provided. Be sure that you correct any words you have spelled incorrectly.

1. _____

2. _____

3. _____

4. _____

5. _____

6. _____

7. _____

8. _____

9. _____

10. _____

11. _____

12. _____

13. _____

14. _____

15. _____

16. _____

17. _____

18. _____

19. _____

20. _____

21. _____

22. _____

23. _____

24. _____

25. _____

Using your words:

Choose ten of today's spelling words and use them in a paragraph, silly story or poem.

_____

_____

_____

_____

_____

_____

_____

_____

_____

_____

Day 59

Spelling Lesson:

As you hear them, write the spelling words for the day in the space provided. Be sure that you correct any words you have spelled incorrectly.

1. _____

2. _____

3. _____

4. _____

5. _____

6. _____

7. _____

8. _____

9. _____

10. _____

11. _____

12. _____

13. _____

14. _____

15. _____

16. _____

17. _____

18. _____

19. _____

20. _____

21. _____

22. _____

23. _____

24. _____

25. _____

Using your words:

Make as many words as you can from the following word.

peculiarity

Day 60

Spelling Lesson:

As you hear them, write the spelling words for the day in the space provided. Be sure that you correct any words you have spelled incorrectly.

1. _____

2. _____

3. _____

4. _____

5. _____

6. _____

7. _____

8. _____

9. _____

10. _____

11. _____

12. _____

13. _____

14. _____

15. _____

16. _____

17. _____

18. _____

19. _____

20. _____

21. _____

22. _____

23. _____

24. _____

25. _____

Using Your Words:

```
P  T  M  T  I  H  C  P  R  W  P  K  Q  S  N  P  U  I
P  E  U  F  K  N  B  A  O  Y  W  O  A  W  V  H  N  B
Z  R  D  A  Y  S  T  U  T  L  R  J  L  D  I  U  F  P
O  H  O  L  M  C  M  E  R  E  A  N  A  C  C  R  A  F
B  R  C  P  A  U  L  P  R  G  R  R  U  Z  A  R  M  R
E  Y  A  G  E  R  P  I  Q  S  L  P  I  U  R  Y  I  I
G  X  C  Q  K  R  S  M  N  Z  T  A  I  T  S  I  L  A
G  K  C  R  G  Y  T  V  E  E  U  E  R  L  Y  N  I  R
A  E  H  S  Q  I  R  I  B  A  A  W  L  I  L  G  A  S
R  V  G  H  B  N  D  E  E  D  Q  R  P  L  E  A  R  Q
S  U  H  A  Y  G  Y  E  H  S  X  X  J  L  A  S  R  N
Q  D  C  P  R  K  Q  C  O  P  I  E  R  S  P  R  X  S
```

Find the following words in the puzzle.
Words are hidden → ↓ and ↘ .

BEGGARS	HURRYING	PROPERTIES
BURGLARIES	INTERSTELLAR	SCURRYING
CATERPILLARS	LINEAR	UNFAMILIAR
COPIERS	PEDLARS	VICARS
FRIARS	POLARITY	

Day 61

Spelling Lesson:

As you hear them, write the spelling words for the day in the space provided. Be sure that you correct any words you have spelled incorrectly.

1. _____

2. _____

3. _____

4. _____

5. _____

6. _____

7. _____

8. _____

9. _____

10. _____

11. _____

12. _____

13. _____

14. _____

15. _____

16. _____

17. _____

18. _____

19. _____

20. _____

21. _____

22. _____

23. _____

24. _____

25. _____

Using Your Words:

Fill in the blanks with words from today's spelling list.

1. May I _____ you a drink?

2. Please _____ the money to my account.

3. What is your _____?

4. It takes _____ to move a heavy weight.

5. The _____ was soon over.

6. A _____ is a shape with three sides.

7. _____ is the opening to the Mediterranean Sea.

8. We must agree to _____ in our beliefs.

9. What may we _____ from your suggestion?

10. That tree is a _____.

Day 62

Spelling Lesson:

As you hear them, write the spelling words for the day in the space provided. Be sure that you correct any words you have spelled incorrectly.

1. _____

2. _____

3. _____

4. _____

5. _____

6. _____

7. _____

8. _____

9. _____

10. _____

11. _____

12. _____

13. _____

14. _____

15. _____

16. _____

17. _____

18. _____

19. _____

20. _____

21. _____

22. _____

23. _____

24. _____

25. _____

Using your words:

Choose ten of today's spelling words and use them in a paragraph, silly story or poem.

_____

_____

_____

_____

_____

_____

_____

_____

_____

Day 63

Spelling Lesson:

As you hear them, write the spelling words for the day in the space provided. Be sure that you correct any words you have spelled incorrectly.

1. _____

2. _____

3. _____

4. _____

5. _____

6. _____

7. _____

8. _____

9. _____

10. _____

11. _____

12. _____

13. _____

14. _____

15. _____

16. _____

17. _____

18. _____

19. _____

20. _____

21. _____

22. _____

23. _____

24. _____

25. _____

Using your words:

List as many words as you can that have the following letters (in order) in them.

ular; ence

Day 64

Spelling Lesson:

As you hear them, write the spelling words for the day in the space provided. Be sure that you correct any words you have spelled incorrectly.

1. _____

2. _____

3. _____

4. _____

5. _____

6. _____

7. _____

8. _____

9. _____

10. _____

11. _____

12. _____

13. _____

14. _____

15. _____

16. _____

17. _____

18. _____

19. _____

20. _____

21. _____

22. _____

23. _____

24. _____

25. _____

Using your words:

Can You  find the Words?

```
Z  G  M  L  P  Z  H  M  O  R  T  A  R  S  F  N  T  J
I  M  R  U  N  O  D  M  Z  V  Z  Q  F  U  W  I  O  O
N  H  N  O  S  X  P  A  A  O  I  W  V  F  U  N  F  C
F  J  T  W  C  C  X  U  U  J  N  D  F  F  J  F  F  U
E  T  U  A  U  E  U  L  L  B  R  H  W  E  G  E  E  L
R  G  U  G  F  M  R  L  X  A  E  Q  H  R  U  R  R  A
R  G  R  B  U  H  V  I  A  C  T  R  U  I  T  E  I  R
I  I  D  A  E  L  G  T  E  R  C  I  S  N  B  N  N  I
N  S  A  X  I  R  A  S  W  S  I  V  O  G  G  C  G  T
G  J  W  O  E  N  S  R  D  J  X  T  F  N  S  E  A  Y
L  Y  E  J  C  R  M  Q  O  R  F  L  Y  O  A  I  Y  V
P  R  E  F  E  R  R  I  N  G  Q  Z  X  J  N  V  H  Y
```

Find the following words in the puzzle.
Words are hidden → ↓ and ↘ .

DAUBERS   JOCULARITY   POPULATION
GRAIN   JUGULAR   PREFERRING
GROCERIES   MORTAR   SUFFERING
INFERENCE   MUSCULARITY   TUBERS
INFERRING   OFFERING

Day 65

Spelling Lesson:

As you hear them, write the spelling words for the day in the space provided. Be sure that you correct any words you have spelled incorrectly.

1. _____

2. _____

3. _____

4. _____

5. _____

6. _____

7. _____

8. _____

9. _____

10. _____

11. _____

12. _____

13. _____

14. _____

15. _____

16. _____

17. _____

18. _____

19. _____

20. _____

21. _____

22. _____

23. _____

24. _____

25. _____

Using your words:

List as many words as you can that have the following letters (in order) in them.

erry; arry

Day 66

As you hear them, write the spelling words for the day in the space provided. Be sure that you correct any words you have spelled incorrectly.

1. _____

2. _____

3. _____

4. _____

5. _____

6. _____

7. _____

8. _____

9. _____

10. _____

11. _____

12. _____

13. _____

14. _____

15. _____

16. _____

17. _____

18. _____

19. _____

20. _____

21. _____

22. _____

23. _____

24. _____

25. _____

Using Your Words:

Fill in the blanks with words from today's spelling list.

1. Cars are carried across the river by _____.

2. Some people keep _____ as pets.

3. We went out into the woods to collect _____.

4. A dog _____ bones in the yard.

5. The painting portrayed three angelic _____.

6. The mistake resulted from a _____ error.

7. The sundaes are topped with _____.

8. He _____ his father's fortune, according to the will.

9. We took rides in _____ in New York City.

10. They drill for oil using _____

Day 67

As you hear them, write the spelling words for the day in the space provided. Be sure that you correct any words you have spelled incorrectly.

1. _____

2. _____

3. _____

4. _____

5. _____

6. _____

7. _____

8. _____

9. _____

10. _____

11. _____

12. _____

13. _____

14. _____

15. _____

16. _____

17. _____

18. _____

19. _____

20. _____

21. _____

22. _____

23. _____

24. _____

25. _____

Using your words:

Unscramble these:

1. rifered   _____

2. ribued   _____

3. icdrear   _____

4. orserr   _____

5. erhi   _____

6. hseidehcr   _____

7. ogrrnhenebi   _____

8. erbcuhim   _____

9. rbreira   _____

10. dnierergr   _____

Day 68

As you hear them, write the spelling words for the day in the space provided. Be sure that you correct any words you have spelled incorrectly.

1. _____   14. _____

2. _____   15. _____

3. _____   16. _____

4. _____   17. _____

5. _____   18. _____

6. _____   19. _____

7. _____   20. _____

8. _____   21. _____

9. _____   22. _____

10. _____   23. _____

11. _____   24. _____

12. _____   25. _____

13. _____

Using your words:

Can You  find the Words?

```
T  P  D  D  H  M  D  P  C  F  P  V  T  C  W  L  C  T
E  B  H  N  T  E  X  E  G  C  A  D  M  A  I  C  E  S
R  U  A  T  G  R  E  U  R  A  K  X  W  R  H  H  A  M
R  R  I  F  T  R  F  E  R  R  E  T  I  N  G  E  U  F
I  Y  R  E  U  I  W  R  C  R  I  M  P  Q  D  R  X  J
B  I  I  R  U  E  K  A  Q  Y  K  N  L  K  P  U  K  U
L  N  E  R  G  S  R  S  G  I  S  M  G  D  Z  B  D  R
E  G  S  Y  X  T  L  U  V  N  F  C  S  E  L  I  G  Y
G  Z  T  I  E  X  S  T  Y  G  D  X  D  U  R  C  X  M
R  W  D  N  E  R  R  I  N  G  Z  N  R  S  M  S  G  N
T  E  L  G  X  Y  K  H  E  I  R  E  S  S  H  N  Q  H
L  L  S  D  E  R  E  L  I  C  T  S  S  S  T  I  O  G
```

Find the following words in the puzzle.
Words are hidden → ↓ and ↘ .

BURYING	ERAS	HEIRESS
CARRYING	ERRING	JURY
CHERUBIC	FERRETING	MERRIEST
DERELICTS	FERRYING	TERRIBLE
DERRINGERS	HAIRIEST	

Day 69

Spelling Lesson:

As you hear them, write the spelling words for the day in the space provided. Be sure that you correct any words you have spelled incorrectly.

1. _____

2. _____

3. _____

4. _____

5. _____

6. _____

7. _____

8. _____

9. _____

10. _____

11. _____

12. _____

13. _____

14. _____

15. _____

16. _____

17. _____

18. _____

19. _____

20. _____

21. _____

22. _____

23. _____

24. _____

25. _____

Using your words:

Make as many words as you can with the following word in them.

or

Day 70

Spelling Lesson:

As you hear them, write the spelling words for the day in the space provided. Be sure that you correct any words you have spelled incorrectly.

1. _____

2. _____

3. _____

4. _____

5. _____

6. _____

7. _____

8. _____

9. _____

10. _____

11. _____

12. _____

13. _____

14. _____

15. _____

16. _____

17. _____

18. _____

19. _____

20. _____

21. _____

22. _____

23. _____

24. _____

25. _____

Using your words:

Fill in the blanks with words from today's spelling list.

1. My football team is called the _____.

2. Submarines use _____ to see while submerged.

3. Animals often defend their _____.

4. A plant _____ without water.

5. A great many _____ write just one book.

6. What are the _____ of your arguments?

7. We didn't know the _____ of the course we took.

8. Drop the _____ to secure the boat.

9. The roar of a lion _____ its prey.

10. The _____ will be graduating soon.

Day 71

As you hear them, write the spelling words for the day in the space provided. Be sure that you correct any words you have spelled incorrectly.

1. _____

2. _____

3. _____

4. _____

5. _____

6. _____

7. _____

8. _____

9. _____

10. _____

11. _____

12. _____

13. _____

14. _____

15. _____

16. _____

17. _____

18. _____

19. _____

20. _____

21. _____

22. _____

23. _____

24. _____

25. _____

Using your words:

Unscramble these:

1. poeulisr   _____

2. lerhipeabs   _____

3. freeidvi   _____

4. echrogaan   _____

5. itrseniyo   _____

6. pioutieyrrs   _____

7. lbeirrte   _____

8. eermitd   _____

9. haetstirp   _____

10. teorniri   _____

Day 72

Spelling Lesson:

As you hear them, write the spelling words for the day in the space provided. Be sure that you correct any words you have spelled incorrectly.

1. _____

2. _____

3. _____

4. _____

5. _____

6. _____

7. _____

8. _____

9. _____

10. _____

11. _____

12. _____

13. _____

14. _____

15. _____

16. _____

17. _____

18. _____

19. _____

20. _____

21. _____

22. _____

23. _____

24. _____

25. _____

Using your words:

Choose ten of today's spelling words and use them in a paragraph, silly story or poem.

_____

_____

_____

_____

_____

_____

_____

_____

_____

_____

Sequential Spelling Level 5 - Student Workbook

Day 73

Spelling Lesson:

As you hear them, write the spelling words for the day in the space provided. Be sure that you correct any words you have spelled incorrectly.

1. _____

2. _____

3. _____

4. _____

5. _____

6. _____

7. _____

8. _____

9. _____

10. _____

11. _____

12. _____

13. _____

14. _____

15. _____

16. _____

17. _____

18. _____

19. _____

20. _____

21. _____

22. _____

23. _____

24. _____

25. _____

Using your words:

Make as many words as you can from the following word.

honorable

Day 74

Spelling Lesson:

As you hear them, write the spelling words for the day in the space provided. Be sure that you correct any words you have spelled incorrectly.

1. _____

2. _____

3. _____

4. _____

5. _____

6. _____

7. _____

8. _____

9. _____

10. _____

11. _____

12. _____

13. _____

14. _____

15. _____

16. _____

17. _____

18. _____

19. _____

20. _____

21. _____

22. _____

23. _____

24. _____

25. _____

Using your words:

Use a dictionary to find the meanings of these words and then use them in a sentence.

1.squalid

2.bachelors

3.gaolers

4.clamors

5.tumors

6.tenors

7.dishonors

8.governors

Sequential Spelling Level 5 - Student Workbook

Day 75

As you hear them, write the spelling words for the day in the space provided. Be sure that you correct any words you have spelled incorrectly.

1. _____

2. _____

3. _____

4. _____

5. _____

6. _____

7. _____

8. _____

9. _____

10. _____

11. _____

12. _____

13. _____

14. _____

15. _____

16. _____

17. _____

18. _____

19. _____

20. _____

21. _____

22. _____

23. _____

24. _____

25. _____

Using your words:

Fill in the blanks with words from today's spelling list.

1. I was selected as a _____.

2. Steam is water turned to _____.

3. The workers _____ for higher pay.

4. The committee _____ the out-going chairman's service.

5. The soldiers made a _____ stand.

6. An _____ vehicle is called a tank.

7. How many votes are needed for a _____ on the motion?

8. Did you hear the latest _____.

9. The soldier received a _____ discharge for cowardice.

10. We went to visit _____ to see Bethlehem.

Day 76

As you hear them, write the spelling words for the day in the space provided. Be sure that you correct any words you have spelled incorrectly.

1. _____

2. _____

3. _____

4. _____

5. _____

6. _____

7. _____

8. _____

9. _____

10. _____

11. _____

12. _____

13. _____

14. _____

15. _____

16. _____

17. _____

18. _____

19. _____

20. _____

21. _____

22. _____

23. _____

24. _____

25. _____

Using your words:

```
V  T  R  C  O  L  O  R  I  N  G  V  Q  D  Y  E  L  A
S  P  C  L  A  M  O  R  I  N  G  A  A  W  F  G  A  T
P  J  T  D  I  V  I  S  O  R  S  L  A  R  S  J  S  T
D  J  U  R  O  R  S  Z  O  F  A  I  R  N  C  A  A  F
D  I  S  H  O  N  O  R  I  N  G  A  M  N  Z  R  G  S
Q  H  U  O  J  X  N  F  M  Y  R  N  O  T  P  U  N  M
B  E  Y  H  A  G  E  J  S  O  Z  T  R  W  C  M  A  H
C  N  C  M  M  F  P  G  F  F  R  L  Y  W  V  O  R  U
E  H  U  M  O  U  R  O  U  S  L  Y  Q  D  P  R  W  S
H  V  A  P  O  R  S  J  Q  C  W  M  W  D  D  S  H  X
M  W  H  O  N  O  R  I  N  G  J  U  A  N  I  T  A  B
G  Q  D  C  J  K  U  R  Z  J  D  S  E  A  N  G  A  T
```

Find the following words in the puzzle.
Words are hidden → ↓ and ↘ .

ARMORY	HONORING	RUMORS
CLAMORING	HUMOUROUSLY	SEAN
COLORING	JUANITA	VALIANTLY
DISHONORING	JURORS	VAPORS
DIVISORS	LASAGNA	

Day 77

As you hear them, write the spelling words for the day in the space provided. Be sure that you correct any words you have spelled incorrectly.

1. _____

2. _____

3. _____

4. _____

5. _____

6. _____

7. _____

8. _____

9. _____

10. _____

11. _____

12. _____

13. _____

14. _____

15. _____

16. _____

17. _____

18. _____

19. _____

20. _____

21. _____

22. _____

23. _____

24. _____

25. _____

Using your words:

Choose ten words from today's spelling list and use each in a sentence.

1._____

_____

2._____

_____

3._____

_____

4._____

_____

5._____

_____

6._____

_____

7._____

_____

8._____

_____

9._____

_____

10._____

Day 78

As you hear them, write the spelling words for the day in the space provided. Be sure that you correct any words you have spelled incorrectly.

1. _____

2. _____

3. _____

4. _____

5. _____

6. _____

7. _____

8. _____

9. _____

10. _____

11. _____

12. _____

13. _____

14. _____

15. _____

16. _____

17. _____

18. _____

19. _____

20. _____

21. _____

22. _____

23. _____

24. _____

25. _____

Using your words:

Unscramble these:

1. sserirpsvuo _____

2. rruoscs _____

3. serccussos _____

4. sporsseofr _____

5. mraiotsed _____

6. strllaoiga _____

7. inoritcdsa _____

8. cosrteorpla _____

9. ospsosperr _____

10. riossssc _____

Day 79

As you hear them, write the spelling words for the day in the space provided. Be sure that you correct any words you have spelled incorrectly.

1. _____

2. _____

3. _____

4. _____

5. _____

6. _____

7. _____

8. _____

9. _____

10. _____

11. _____

12. _____

13. _____

14. _____

15. _____

16. _____

17. _____

18. _____

19. _____

20. _____

21. _____

22. _____

23. _____

24. _____

25. _____

Using your words:

Fill in the blanks with words from today's spelling list.

1. I filled the _____ position at work.

2. Janice _____ a family from overseas.

3. You must work hard to get a good _____

4. The _____ did not leak from the reactor.

5. The policeman cited me for a _____ of the parking rules.

6. The heavy clouds were _____ .

7. The room needs better _____ because it smells.

8. Your credentials are very _____ !

9. The dictator _____ the press.

10. Our review was only _____ , very brief.

Spelling Lesson:

As you hear them, write the spelling words for the day in the space provided. Be sure that you correct any words you have spelled incorrectly.

1. _____

2. _____

3. _____

4. _____

5. _____

6. _____

7. _____

8. _____

9. _____

10. _____

11. _____

12. _____

13. _____

14. _____

15. _____

16. _____

17. _____

18. _____

19. _____

20. _____

21. _____

22. _____

23. _____

24. _____

25. _____

Using your words

Make as many words as you can with the following letters (in order) in them.

ion

Evaluation Test #2

Fill in the blanks with the missing letters.

1. It seemed a mir_____ when Chicago won the World Series.

2. The patient made a mirac_____ recovery.

3. The two countries signed a non-aggression p_____ .

4. Sugar attr_____ ants.

5. Do you like previews of coming attr_____ ?

6. We stand corr_____ .

7. Do you need dir_____ on how to get there?

8. You really should wear prot_____ headgear.

9. We attended three l_____ last year.

10. That patient is on a restr_____ diet.

11. How many of the psychic's pred_____ came true?

12. How many heat d_____ are there in this room?

13. My brother works for a constr_____ company.

14. I think my sister has a real attit_____ problem.

15. How do you think I arrived at that concl_____ ?

16. Does every grave have a t_____ stone?

17. Have you seen the latest house des_____ ?

18. Our national debt seems to keep incr_____ .

19. I don't like to be threat_____ by anyone.

20. We gave them new sw_____ for their anniversary.

Day 81

Spelling Lesson:

As you hear them, write the spelling words for the day in the space provided. Be sure that you correct any words you have spelled incorrectly.

1. _____

2. _____

3. _____

4. _____

5. _____

6. _____

7. _____

8. _____

9. _____

10. _____

11. _____

12. _____

13. _____

14. _____

15. _____

16. _____

17. _____

18. _____

19. _____

20. _____

21. _____

22. _____

23. _____

24. _____

25. _____

Using your words:

Fill in the blanks with words from today's spelling list.

1. I like building things, so I will become an _____.

2. We took the _____ to the tenth floor.

3. The words of the _____ stirred us all!

4. The foul ball hit a _____ .

5. The _____ hired an _____ to review his sermons.

6. The _____ shaved with a _____ each morning before leaving for Capitol Hill.

7. We need an _____ to help settle this dispute.

8. What _____ of ice cream do you prefer?

9. The boys left the mess for the _____ to clean up.

10. A _____ is someone who lends money.

Day 82

As you hear them, write the spelling words for the day in the space provided. Be sure that you correct any words you have spelled incorrectly.

1. _____

2. _____

3. _____

4. _____

5. _____

6. _____

7. _____

8. _____

9. _____

10. _____

11. _____

12. _____

13. _____

14. _____

15. _____

16. _____

17. _____

18. _____

19. _____

20. _____

21. _____

22. _____

23. _____

24. _____

25. _____

Using your words:

Unscramble these:

1. caoresrdto _____

2. aenstsro _____

3. trsitora _____

4. trlovaese _____

5. sorsitvi _____

6. onjitars _____

7. otspars _____

8. sorviurvs _____

9. ooenttrrms _____

10. trosora _____

Day 83

As you hear them, write the spelling words for the day in the space provided. Be sure that you correct any words you have spelled incorrectly.

1. _____

2. _____

3. _____

4. _____

5. _____

6. _____

7. _____

8. _____

9. _____

10. _____

11. _____

12. _____

13. _____

14. _____

15. _____

16. _____

17. _____

18. _____

19. _____

20. _____

21. _____

22. _____

23. _____

24. _____

25. _____

Using your words:

Choose ten words from today's spelling list and use each in a sentence.

1. _____

_____

2. _____

_____

3. _____

_____

4. _____

_____

5. _____

_____

6. _____

_____

7. _____

_____

8. _____

_____

9. _____

_____

10. _____

_____

Sequential Spelling Level 5 - Student Workbook

Spelling Lesson:

As you hear them, write the spelling words for the day in the space provided. Be sure that you correct any words you have spelled incorrectly.

1. _____

2. _____

3. _____

4. _____

5. _____

6. _____

7. _____

8. _____

9. _____

10. _____

11. _____

12. _____

13. _____

14. _____

15. _____

16. _____

17. _____

18. _____

19. _____

20. _____

21. _____

22. _____

23. _____

24. _____

25. _____

Using your words:

```
D V Z S F C R H Y M E S I S M B I Q
E O A A F U V S A L M O N P O D U U
C R U V R L W T H R Q X V E M W V F
O A D O G T V U O A M V E C B M R A
R T I R D I O K D X G R N T W E H V
A I T I Y V K A X S S S T A G N Y O
T O O N W A X O Q I I M I C E T T R
I N R G Z T E V B E H M O U Y O H I
O I I P J E Q N A V F B N L H R M T
N W U N C D K T P E G S G A U S S E
Z E M A F C C R A S B A A R R H D Q
J U S O L D I E R S H C Q M F M J V
```

Find the following words in the puzzle.
Words are hidden → ↓ and ↘ .

AUDITORIUM   MENTORS   SAVORING
CULTIVATED   ORATION   SIEVES
DECORATION   RHYMES   SOLDIERS
FAVORITE   RHYTHMS   SPECTACULAR
INVENTION   SALMON

Day 85

As you hear them, write the spelling words for the day in the space provided. Be sure that you correct any words you have spelled incorrectly.

1. _____

2. _____

3. _____

4. _____

5. _____

6. _____

7. _____

8. _____

9. _____

10. _____

11. _____

12. _____

13. _____

14. _____

15. _____

16. _____

17. _____

18. _____

19. _____

20. _____

21. _____

22. _____

23. _____

24. _____

25. _____

Using your words:

Make as many words as you can from the following word.

manoeuvre

Day 86

Spelling Lesson:

As you hear them, write the spelling words for the day in the space provided. Be sure that you correct any words you have spelled incorrectly.

1. _____

2. _____

3. _____

4. _____

5. _____

6. _____

7. _____

8. _____

9. _____

10. _____

11. _____

12. _____

13. _____

14. _____

15. _____

16. _____

17. _____

18. _____

19. _____

20. _____

21. _____

22. _____

23. _____

24. _____

25. _____

Using your words:

Unscramble these:

1. triluacve _____

2. sarec _____

3. aseamsscr _____

4. olrsuust _____

5. lemrbsa _____

6. bsitudred _____

7. ebalrms _____

8. lsucrste _____

9. urnab _____

10. abelrsg _____

Day 87

Spelling Lesson:

As you hear them, write the spelling words for the day in the space provided. Be sure that you correct any words you have spelled incorrectly.

1. _____

2. _____

3. _____

4. _____

5. _____

6. _____

7. _____

8. _____

9. _____

10. _____

11. _____

12. _____

13. _____

14. _____

15. _____

16. _____

17. _____

18. _____

19. _____

20. _____

21. _____

22. _____

23. _____

24. _____

25. _____

Using your words:

Choose ten of today's spelling words and use them in a paragraph, silly story or poem.

_____

_____

_____

_____

_____

_____

_____

_____

_____

_____

Day 88

Spelling Lesson:

As you hear them, write the spelling words for the day in the space provided. Be sure that you correct any words you have spelled incorrectly.

1. _____

2. _____

3. _____

4. _____

5. _____

6. _____

7. _____

8. _____

9. _____

10. _____

11. _____

12. _____

13. _____

14. _____

15. _____

16. _____

17. _____

18. _____

19. _____

20. _____

21. _____

22. _____

23. _____

24. _____

25. _____

Using your words:

Choose ten words from today's spelling list and use each in a sentence.

1._____

_____

2._____

_____

3._____

_____

4._____

_____

5._____

_____

6._____

_____

7._____

_____

8._____

_____

9._____

_____

10._____

_____

Day 89

As you hear them, write the spelling words for the day in the space provided. Be sure that you correct any words you have spelled incorrectly.

1. _____

2. _____

3. _____

4. _____

5. _____

6. _____

7. _____

8. _____

9. _____

10. _____

11. _____

12. _____

13. _____

14. _____

15. _____

16. _____

17. _____

18. _____

19. _____

20. _____

21. _____

22. _____

23. _____

24. _____

25. _____

Using your words:

Choose ten of today's spelling words and use them in a paragraph, silly story or poem.

_____

_____

_____

_____

_____

_____

_____

_____

_____

_____

Day 90

As you hear them, write the spelling words for the day in the space provided. Be sure that you correct any words you have spelled incorrectly.

1. _____

2. _____

3. _____

4. _____

5. _____

6. _____

7. _____

8. _____

9. _____

10. _____

11. _____

12. _____

13. _____

14. _____

15. _____

16. _____

17. _____

18. _____

19. _____

20. _____

21. _____

22. _____

23. _____

24. _____

25. _____

Using your words:

Use each of these words correctly in a sentence.

1. scarcely _____

_____

2. commercial _____

_____

3. enforces _____

_____

4. outsources _____

_____

5. researches _____

_____

6. searchlights _____

_____

7. scorches _____

_____

8. hereafter _____

_____

9. adheres _____

_____

10. hemisphere _____

_____

Day 91

Spelling Lesson:

As you hear them, write the spelling words for the day in the space provided. Be sure that you correct any words you have spelled incorrectly.

1. _____

2. _____

3. _____

4. _____

5. _____

6. _____

7. _____

8. _____

9. _____

10. _____

11. _____

12. _____

13. _____

14. _____

15. _____

16. _____

17. _____

18. _____

19. _____

20. _____

21. _____

22. _____

23. _____

24. _____

25. _____

Using your words:

Fill in the blanks with words from today's spelling list.

1. The forest fire left the earth _____.

2. The police _____ the curfew strictly.

3. We bought a _____ on our trip.

4. _____ can really ruin a good TV show.

5. They _____ the levee before the storm.

6. The birds _____ on the powerline.

7. Did the _____ have an apprentice?

8. We left the _____ on for you.

9. He made a _____ arguement for change.

10. The spaghetti _____ to the wall where we threw it.

Day 92

As you hear them, write the spelling words for the day in the space provided. Be sure that you correct any words you have spelled incorrectly.

1. _____

2. _____

3. _____

4. _____

5. _____

6. _____

7. _____

8. _____

9. _____

10. _____

11. _____

12. _____

13. _____

14. _____

15. _____

16. _____

17. _____

18. _____

19. _____

20. _____

21. _____

22. _____

23. _____

24. _____

25. _____

Using your words

```
U A D H E S I O N X C V H P E V O F
N A I S O R C E R Y B I F N N P F H
F O R C I N G S Z I X Q M X F O T B
A C Q K G J T R O P W O D A O G O N
R E S O U R C E F U L L Y T R J R I
Z S E A R C H I N G V I Y H C F C O
Q T O N G U E S N U Q E N L I I H D
S T R A T O S P H E R E N P N Z I L
C M N L T O W A R D S K E I G I N C
P T O R C H L I G H T Y E C R N G A
L P X G P I E R C I N G T L X S D Q
C O M M E R C I A L L Y B P U E G K
```

Find the following words in the puzzle.
Words are hidden → ↓ and ↘ .

ADHESION
COMMERCIALLY
ENFORCING
FORCING
PIERCING

RESOURCEFULLY
SEARCHING
SORCERY
SOUVENIRS
STRATOSPHERE

TONGUES
TORCHING
TORCHLIGHT
TOWARDS

Day 93

As you hear them, write the spelling words for the day in the space provided. Be sure that you correct any words you have spelled incorrectly.

1. _____

2. _____

3. _____

4. _____

5. _____

6. _____

7. _____

8. _____

9. _____

10. _____

11. _____

12. _____

13. _____

14. _____

15. _____

16. _____

17. _____

18. _____

19. _____

20. _____

21. _____

22. _____

23. _____

24. _____

25. _____

Using your words:

Fill in the blanks with words from today's spelling list.

1. What's the _____ of the match now?

2. You must often _____ to succeed.

3. They smelted the _____ to make pure iron.

4. _____ Perry won the Battle of Mobile Bay.

5. Do not _____ with emergency personnel.

6. Your statement is a _____ expression of your interest.

7. That is an _____ untruth you spoke.

8. The audience called for an _____ at the performance.

9. We all _____ George Washington's service.

10. _____! Watch out for my golfball!

Day 94

As you hear them, write the spelling words for the day in the space provided. Be sure that you correct any words you have spelled incorrectly.

1. _____

2. _____

3. _____

4. _____

5. _____

6. _____

7. _____

8. _____

9. _____

10. _____

11. _____

12. _____

13. _____

14. _____

15. _____

16. _____

17. _____

18. _____

19. _____

20. _____

21. _____

22. _____

23. _____

24. _____

25. _____

Using your words:

List as many words as you can that have the following letters (in order) in them.

ions

_____

_____

_____

_____

_____

_____

_____

_____

_____

_____

_____

Day 95

As you hear them, write the spelling words for the day in the space provided. Be sure that you correct any words you have spelled incorrectly.

1. _____

2. _____

3. _____

4. _____

5. _____

6. _____

7. _____

8. _____

9. _____

10. _____

11. _____

12. _____

13. _____

14. _____

15. _____

16. _____

17. _____

18. _____

19. _____

20. _____

21. _____

22. _____

23. _____

24. _____

25. _____

Using your words:

Choose ten of today's spelling words and use them in a paragraph, silly story or poem.

_____

_____

_____

_____

_____

_____

_____

_____

_____

_____

Day 96

As you hear them, write the spelling words for the day in the space provided. Be sure that you correct any words you have spelled incorrectly.

1. _____

2. _____

3. _____

4. _____

5. _____

6. _____

7. _____

8. _____

9. _____

10. _____

11. _____

12. _____

13. _____

14. _____

15. _____

16. _____

17. _____

18. _____

19. _____

20. _____

21. _____

22. _____

23. _____

24. _____

25. _____

Using your words:

Make a rhyme or silly story using ten of today's spelling words.

_____

_____

_____

_____

_____

_____

_____

_____

_____

_____

Day 97

Spelling Lesson:

As you hear them, write the spelling words for the day in the space provided. Be sure that you correct any words you have spelled incorrectly.

1. _____

2. _____

3. _____

4. _____

5. _____

6. _____

7. _____

8. _____

9. _____

10. _____

11. _____

12. _____

13. _____

14. _____

15. _____

16. _____

17. _____

18. _____

19. _____

20. _____

21. _____

22. _____

23. _____

24. _____

25. _____

Using your words:

Unscramble these:

1. eogr _____

2. heors _____

3. xerlpoe _____

4. ermeoevr _____

5. rcniavore _____

6. fusgdiire _____

7. oetsrer _____

8. ufrieal _____

9. onser _____

10. oiprlme _____

Sequential Spelling Level 5 - Student Workbook

Day 98

As you hear them, write the spelling words for the day in the space provided. Be sure that you correct any words you have spelled incorrectly.

1. _____

2. _____

3. _____

4. _____

5. _____

6. _____

7. _____

8. _____

9. _____

10. _____

11. _____

12. _____

13. _____

14. _____

15. _____

16. _____

17. _____

18. _____

19. _____

20. _____

21. _____

22. _____

23. _____

24. _____

25. _____

Using your words:

Choose ten of today's spelling words and use them in a paragraph, silly story or poem.

_____

_____

_____

_____

_____

_____

_____

_____

_____

Day 99

As you hear them, write the spelling words for the day in the space provided. Be sure that you correct any words you have spelled incorrectly.

1. _____

2. _____

3. _____

4. _____

5. _____

6. _____

7. _____

8. _____

9. _____

10. _____

11. _____

12. _____

13. _____

14. _____

15. _____

16. _____

17. _____

18. _____

19. _____

20. _____

21. _____

22. _____

23. _____

24. _____

25. _____

Using your words:

Can you find the words?

```
W  D  R  U  B  U  F  A  S  H  U  R  H  G  Y  S  S  M
O  E  E  Q  P  A  I  E  E  F  S  N  O  R  E  D  I  C
T  P  S  P  Y  S  G  A  A  G  O  C  F  P  A  Z  N  U
O  L  T  D  A  E  U  S  S  K  J  L  U  W  L  B  G  R
Z  O  O  R  X  C  R  I  H  E  F  Q  K  R  V  B  A  E
M  R  R  C  R  U  E  K  O  X  Y  T  K  L  E  R  P  D
Y  E  E  F  I  R  D  Z  R  R  T  E  M  H  O  D  O  X
C  D  D  Y  R  E  X  B  E  G  V  O  S  N  O  R  R  J
O  T  G  X  D  D  T  N  E  V  E  R  M  O  R  E  E  W
Q  E  Q  E  R  I  J  V  T  Q  A  T  Q  Q  R  A  X  O
L  P  G  O  R  E  D  T  X  Z  E  I  W  S  Y  E  X  S
R  O  Y  T  E  S  J  W  S  T  O  R  E  D  B  U  K  P
```

Find the following words in the puzzle.
Words are hidden → ↓ and ↘ .

CURED   FOLKLORE   SECURED
CURED   GORED   SINGAPORE
DEPLORED   NEVERMORE   SNORED
EYESORE   RESTORED   STORED
FIGURED   SEASHORE

Day 100

Spelling Lesson:

As you hear them, write the spelling words for the day in the space provided. Be sure that you correct any words you have spelled incorrectly.

1. _____

2. _____

3. _____

4. _____

5. _____

6. _____

7. _____

8. _____

9. _____

10. _____

11. _____

12. _____

13. _____

14. _____

15. _____

16. _____

17. _____

18. _____

19. _____

20. _____

21. _____

22. _____

23. _____

24. _____

25. _____

Using your words:

Choose at least ten words from your spelling list and use them in a rhyme, silly story or sentences.

_____

_____

_____

_____

_____

_____

_____

_____

_____

_____

_____

Sequential Spelling Level 5 - Student Workbook

Day 101

As you hear them, write the spelling words for the day in the space provided. Be sure that you correct any words you have spelled incorrectly.

1. _____

2. _____

3. _____

4. _____

5. _____

6. _____

7. _____

8. _____

9. _____

10. _____

11. _____

12. _____

13. _____

14. _____

15. _____

16. _____

17. _____

18. _____

19. _____

20. _____

21. _____

22. _____

23. _____

24. _____

25. _____

Using your words:

List as many words as you can which have the following letters (in order) in them.

ure

Spelling Lesson:

As you hear them, write the spelling words for the day in the space provided. Be sure that you correct any words you have spelled incorrectly.

1. _____

2. _____

3. _____

4. _____

5. _____

6. _____

7. _____

8. _____

9. _____

10. _____

11. _____

12. _____

13. _____

14. _____

15. _____

16. _____

17. _____

18. _____

19. _____

20. _____

21. _____

22. _____

23. _____

24. _____

25. _____

Using Your Words:

Fill in the blanks with words from today's spelling list.

1. Medieval lords had _____ to work their lands.

2. A careful man _____ the situation before acting.

3. I do not find your perfume _____.

4. Can you put up some _____ for us to shoot at?

5. We left _____ the intermission.

6. There were _____ for the water park.

7. Few people have _____ any more.

8. There are many _____ in <u>The Hobbit</u>.

9. _____ are good to wear in winter.

10. He fishs for bass with _____.

Day 103

Spelling Lesson:

As you hear them, write the spelling words for the day in the space provided. Be sure that you correct any words you have spelled incorrectly.

1. _____

2. _____

3. _____

4. _____

5. _____

6. _____

7. _____

8. _____

9. _____

10. _____

11. _____

12. _____

13. _____

14. _____

15. _____

16. _____

17. _____

18. _____

19. _____

20. _____

21. _____

22. _____

23. _____

24. _____

25. _____

Using Your Words

Unscramble these:

1. orutdain   _____

2. ercepduor   _____

3. jynriu   _____

4. sdtiuveer   _____

5. vreatvepries _____

6. tayerobrosv _____

7. lderu   _____

8. erswved   _____

9. eddsreev   _____

10. tategdre   _____

Day 104

As you hear them, write the spelling words for the day in the space provided. Be sure that you correct any words you have spelled incorrectly.

1. _____

2. _____

3. _____

4. _____

5. _____

6. _____

7. _____

8. _____

9. _____

10. _____

11. _____

12. _____

13. _____

14. _____

15. _____

16. _____

17. _____

18. _____

19. _____

20. _____

21. _____

22. _____

23. _____

24. _____

25. _____

Using Your Words:

Make as many words as you can from the following word.

preservation

Day 105

Spelling Lesson:

As you hear them, write the spelling words for the day in the space provided. Be sure that you correct any words you have spelled incorrectly.

1. _____

2. _____

3. _____

4. _____

5. _____

6. _____

7. _____

8. _____

9. _____

10. _____

11. _____

12. _____

13. _____

14. _____

15. _____

16. _____

17. _____

18. _____

19. _____

20. _____

21. _____

22. _____

23. _____

24. _____

25. _____

Using Your Words:

Fill in the blanks with words from today's spelling list.

1. You should never _____ your work.

2. The Titanic hit an _____ and sank.

3. Is your _____ too heavy?.

4. The submarine will _____ once it is at sea.

5. We have to _____ on to the highway.

6. His _____ irritated his teacher.

7. Did you _____ at the factory last night?

8. We need to _____ some coffee to get _____

   in the morning.

9. Did you _____ the chicken for dinner?

10. The SEC prohibited the _____.

Spelling Lesson:

As you hear them, write the spelling words for the day in the space provided. Be sure that you correct any words you have spelled incorrectly.

1. _____

2. _____

3. _____

4. _____

5. _____

6. _____

7. _____

8. _____

9. _____

10. _____

11. _____

12. _____

13. _____

14. _____

15. _____

16. _____

17. _____

18. _____

19. _____

20. _____

21. _____

22. _____

23. _____

24. _____

25. _____

Using your words:

List as many words as you can that have the following letters (in order) in them.

erg

ork

Spelling Lesson:

As you hear them, write the spelling words for the day in the space provided. Be sure that you correct any words you have spelled incorrectly.

1. _____

2. _____

3. _____

4. _____

5. _____

6. _____

7. _____

8. _____

9. _____

10. _____

11. _____

12. _____

13. _____

14. _____

15. _____

16. _____

17. _____

18. _____

19. _____

20. _____

21. _____

22. _____

23. _____

24. _____

25. _____

Using your words:

Unscramble these:

1. rmcnyegee _____

2. eorgrf _____

3. rgedusebm _____

4. iderk _____

5. rohskroew _____

6. kirhdse _____

7. codrek _____

8. grdeem _____

9. ertskeip _____

10. eregdme _____

Spelling Lesson:

As you hear them, write the spelling words for the day in the space provided. Be sure that you correct any words you have spelled incorrectly.

1. _____

2. _____

3. _____

4. _____

5. _____

6. _____

7. _____

8. _____

9. _____

10. _____

11. _____

12. _____

13. _____

14. _____

15. _____

16. _____

17. _____

18. _____

19. _____

20. _____

21. _____

22. _____

23. _____

24. _____

25. _____

Using your words

Can You find the Words?

```
Y  L  A  A  I  K  J  C  G  C  Q  L  A  J  Y  A  E  M
V  O  F  X  I  V  H  E  H  D  O  G  K  R  L  X  S  U
R  E  C  D  K  W  A  P  R  F  O  R  G  I  N  G  H  E
E  S  H  R  F  O  M  P  T  K  F  V  K  J  K  V  I  X
M  L  I  D  R  R  B  E  Y  A  I  O  X  I  G  H  R  V
E  G  Y  G  N  K  U  R  O  L  D  N  R  R  N  X  K  L
R  C  A  Y  W  O  R  K  T  W  Q  B  G  G  B  G  I  J
G  L  C  U  N  U  G  I  W  M  W  V  L  J  E  Q  N  E
I  U  H  X  H  T  E  N  B  U  R  G  E  R  C  R  G  R
N  Q  T  T  W  S  R  G  S  M  I  R  K  I  N  G  S  K
G  M  M  E  C  I  D  U  Y  T  Z  A  V  P  X  S  M  Y
Y  U  T  E  Y  M  E  R  G  I  N  G  C  O  U  K  C  K
```

Find the following words in the puzzle.
Words are hidden → ↓ and ↘ .

BURGER   HAMBURGER   SHIRKING
CORKING   JERKING   SMIRKING
EMERGING   JERKY   WORKOUTS
FORGERS   MERGING   YACHT
FORGING   PERKING

Day 109

Spelling Lesson:

As you hear them, write the spelling words for the day in the space provided. Be sure that you correct any words you have spelled incorrectly.

1. _____   14. _____

2. _____   15. _____

3. _____   16. _____

4. _____   17. _____

5. _____   18. _____

6. _____   19. _____

7. _____   20. _____

8. _____   21. _____

9. _____   22. _____

10. _____   23. _____

11. _____   24. _____

12. _____   25. _____

13. _____

Using your words:

Choose ten of today's spelling words and use them in a paragraph, silly story or poem.

_____

_____

_____

_____

_____

_____

_____

_____

_____

_____

Day 110

Spelling Lesson:

As you hear them, write the spelling words for the day in the space provided. Be sure that you correct any words you have spelled incorrectly.

1. _____

2. _____

3. _____

4. _____

5. _____

6. _____

7. _____

8. _____

9. _____

10. _____

11. _____

12. _____

13. _____

14. _____

15. _____

16. _____

17. _____

18. _____

19. _____

20. _____

21. _____

22. _____

23. _____

24. _____

25. _____

Using Your Words:

List as many words as you can with the following letters (in order) in them.

ier

irm

Sequential Spelling Level 5 - Student Workbook

Day 111

As you hear them, write the spelling words for the day in the space provided. Be sure that you correct any words you have spelled incorrectly.

1. _____

2. _____

3. _____

4. _____

5. _____

6. _____

7. _____

8. _____

9. _____

10. _____

11. _____

12. _____

13. _____

14. _____

15. _____

16. _____

17. _____

18. _____

19. _____

20. _____

21. _____

22. _____

23. _____

24. _____

25. _____

Using your words:

Choose ten of today's spelling words and use them in a paragraph, silly story or poem.

_____

_____

_____

_____

_____

_____

_____

_____

_____

_____

Day 112

Spelling Lesson:

As you hear them, write the spelling words for the day in the space provided. Be sure that you correct any words you have spelled incorrectly.

1. _____

2. _____

3. _____

4. _____

5. _____

6. _____

7. _____

8. _____

9. _____

10. _____

11. _____

12. _____

13. _____

14. _____

15. _____

16. _____

17. _____

18. _____

19. _____

20. _____

21. _____

22. _____

23. _____

24. _____

25. _____

Using your words:

Choose at least ten words from your spelling list and use each in a sentence.

1._____

_____

2._____

_____

3._____

_____

4._____

_____

5._____

_____

6._____

_____

7._____

_____

8._____

_____

9._____

_____

10._____

_____

Sequential Spelling Level 5 - Student Workbook

Day 113

As you hear them, write the spelling words for the day in the space provided. Be sure that you correct any words you have spelled incorrectly.

1. _____

2. _____

3. _____

4. _____

5. _____

6. _____

7. _____

8. _____

9. _____

10. _____

11. _____

12. _____

13. _____

14. _____

15. _____

16. _____

17. _____

18. _____

19. _____

20. _____

21. _____

22. _____

23. _____

24. _____

25. _____

Using your words:

Choose ten of today's spelling words and use them in a paragraph, silly story or poem.

Day 114

Spelling Lesson:

As you hear them, write the spelling words for the day in the space provided. Be sure that you correct any words you have spelled incorrectly.

1. _____

2. _____

3. _____

4. _____

5. _____

6. _____

7. _____

8. _____

9. _____

10. _____

11. _____

12. _____

13. _____

14. _____

15. _____

16. _____

17. _____

18. _____

19. _____

20. _____

21. _____

22. _____

23. _____

24. _____

25. _____

233

Using your words:

List as many words as you can that have the following letters (in order) in them.

orm

Day 115

Spelling Lesson:

As you hear them, write the spelling words for the day in the space provided. Be sure that you correct any words you have spelled incorrectly.

1. _____

2. _____

3. _____

4. _____

5. _____

6. _____

7. _____

8. _____

9. _____

10. _____

11. _____

12. _____

13. _____

14. _____

15. _____

16. _____

17. _____

18. _____

19. _____

20. _____

21. _____

22. _____

23. _____

24. _____

25. _____

235

Using your words:

Fill in the blanks with words from today's spelling list.

1. The band _____ a concert.

2. Martin Luther started the _____.

3. We had our dog _____ at the vet.

4. What file _____ does the program use?

5. We like _____ in our products.

6. The enemy spread _____ in our country.

7. He is my _____ boss. I have a new one.

8. The product _____ to all the required standards.

9. We put a _____ over our picnic table.

10. The _____ ended with a grand finale.

Day 116

Spelling Lesson:

As you hear them, write the spelling words for the day in the space provided. Be sure that you correct any words you have spelled incorrectly.

1. _____

2. _____

3. _____

4. _____

5. _____

6. _____

7. _____

8. _____

9. _____

10. _____

11. _____

12. _____

13. _____

14. _____

15. _____

16. _____

17. _____

18. _____

19. _____

20. _____

21. _____

22. _____

23. _____

24. _____

25. _____

Using your words

Can You find the Words?

```
N   R   I   X   U   U   U   Z   S   C   A   R   P   I   N   G   N   S
G   E   M   P   U   N   N   F   G   C   M   V   L   O   E   N   O   P
K   F   I   E   X   Q   I   O   T   O   Y   N   U   L   N   Y   O   Q
N   O   N   R   W   O   F   R   M   N   T   X   N   R   O   X   N   W
F   R   F   F   O   Y   O   M   T   F   S   H   I   B   R   Q   E   O
O   M   O   O   R   R   E   A   O   D   I   F   U   M   L   B   R
R   E   R   R   M   Z   M   R   R   R   V   G   O   H   O   E   U   M
M   R   M   M   H   A   I   L   P   M   B   E   R   Y   U   B   Y   I
I   S   A   I   O   O   T   Y   S   I   A   R   M   E   S   U   P   N
N   I   N   N   L   X   Y   Q   D   N   M   Z   S   D   J   R   U   G
G   C   T   G   E   Q   H   P   T   G   D   G   L   F   Y   O   W   U
O   F   R   E   F   O   R   M   I   N   G   A   S   U   F   U   R   E
```

Find the following words in the puzzle.
Words are hidden → ↓ and ↘ .

CARPING	INFORMANT	UNIFORMITY
CONFORMING	PERFORMING	UNIFORMS
ENORMOUS	REFORMERS	WORMHOLE
FORMERLY	REFORMING	WORMING
FORMING	TARPS	

Day 117

As you hear them, write the spelling words for the day in the space provided. Be sure that you correct any words you have spelled incorrectly.

1. _____

2. _____

3. _____

4. _____

5. _____

6. _____

7. _____

8. _____

9. _____

10. _____

11. _____

12. _____

13. _____

14. _____

15. _____

16. _____

17. _____

18. _____

19. _____

20. _____

21. _____

22. _____

23. _____

24. _____

25. _____

Using your words:

List as many words as possible with the following letters (in order) in them.

erse

Day 118

Spelling Lesson:

As you hear them, write the spelling words for the day in the space provided. Be sure that you correct any words you have spelled incorrectly.

1. _____

2. _____

3. _____

4. _____

5. _____

6. _____

7. _____

8. _____

9. _____

10. _____

11. _____

12. _____

13. _____

14. _____

15. _____

16. _____

17. _____

18. _____

19. _____

20. _____

21. _____

22. _____

23. _____

24. _____

25. _____

241

Using your words:

Choose ten of today's spelling words and use them in a paragraph, silly story or poem.

_____

_____

_____

_____

_____

_____

_____

_____

_____

_____

Day 119

As you hear them, write the spelling words for the day in the space provided. Be sure that you correct any words you have spelled incorrectly.

1. _____

2. _____

3. _____

4. _____

5. _____

6. _____

7. _____

8. _____

9. _____

10. _____

11. _____

12. _____

13. _____

14. _____

15. _____

16. _____

17. _____

18. _____

19. _____

20. _____

21. _____

22. _____

23. _____

24. _____

25. _____

Using your words

Fill in the blanks with words from today's spelling list.

1. We _____ the axe.

2. We are practicing water _____.

3. We _____ on the students' need for study.

4. All our costs were _____.

5. The trees are _____ at high altitude.

6. He _____ his soup loudly.

7. All the funds were _____.

8. We _____ our injured ankles after the fall.

9. The duke _____ the king's throne.

10. I am _____ in spelling.

Day 120

As you hear them, write the spelling words for the day in the space provided. Be sure that you correct any words you have spelled incorrectly.

1. _____

2. _____

3. _____

4. _____

5. _____

6. _____

7. _____

8. _____

9. _____

10. _____

11. _____

12. _____

13. _____

14. _____

15. _____

16. _____

17. _____

18. _____

19. _____

20. _____

21. _____

22. _____

23. _____

24. _____

25. _____

Using your words

Make as many words as you can from the following word:

reimbursement

Evaluation Test #3

Fill in the blanks with the missing letters.

1. Do they allow any sp_____ at that event?

2. What inv_____ sparked the modern era?

3. You would think a capital would be in a c_____ location.

4. I hope there isn't another dist_____ at the fair.

5. Do you like to watch comm_____?

6. Our country has many natural res_____.

7. Most people appreciate sinc_____.

8. Curi_____ killed the cat.

9. My confidence in you has been rest_____.

10. My cousin specializes in the rest_____ of antique cars.

11. We made a dinner res_____.

12. Some of my best friends are highly cons_____.

13. Do you know what you should do in an em_____?

14. Would you please stop sm_____.

15. You must take an aff_____ stand.

16. We need some more inf_____.

17. It was an absolutely great perf_____.

18. We need a new pencil sh_____.

19. Did you go to the dress reh_____?

20. I don't remember having that conv_____.

Day 121

Spelling Lesson:

As you hear them, write the spelling words for the day in the space provided. Be sure that you correct any words you have spelled incorrectly.

1. _____

2. _____

3. _____

4. _____

5. _____

6. _____

7. _____

8. _____

9. _____

10. _____

11. _____

12. _____

13. _____

14. _____

15. _____

16. _____

17. _____

18. _____

19. _____

20. _____

21. _____

22. _____

23. _____

24. _____

25. _____

Using your words:

List as many words as you can with the following letters (in order) in them.

rse; ert

_____

_____

_____

_____

_____

_____

_____

_____

_____

_____

Spelling Lesson:

As you hear them, write the spelling words for the day in the space provided. Be sure that you correct any words you have spelled incorrectly.

1. _____

2. _____

3. _____

4. _____

5. _____

6. _____

7. _____

8. _____

9. _____

10. _____

11. _____

12. _____

13. _____

14. _____

15. _____

16. _____

17. _____

18. _____

19. _____

20. _____

21. _____

22. _____

23. _____

24. _____

25. _____

Using your words:

Unscramble these:

1. seremims _____

2. soaercyl _____

3. eshsamr _____

4. darrieh _____

5. eierhrta _____

6. vrtoeig _____

7. tepserx _____

8. rhtisst _____

9. thearhs _____

10. osurecs _____

Day 123

Spelling Lesson:

As you hear them, write the spelling words for the day in the space provided. Be sure that you correct any words you have spelled incorrectly.

1. _____

2. _____

3. _____

4. _____

5. _____

6. _____

7. _____

8. _____

9. _____

10. _____

11. _____

12. _____

13. _____

14. _____

15. _____

16. _____

17. _____

18. _____

19. _____

20. _____

21. _____

22. _____

23. _____

24. _____

25. _____

Using your words

Using a dictionary, find the definitions of these spelling words. Then, use each correctly in a sentence.

1. immersed _____

_____

2. recourse _____

_____

3. impartial _____

_____

4. burst _____

_____

5. Alberta _____

_____

6. sieve _____

_____

7. vertical _____

_____

8. sovereign _____

_____

254

Spelling Lesson:

As you hear them, write the spelling words for the day in the space provided. Be sure that you correct any words you have spelled incorrectly.

1. _____

2. _____

3. _____

4. _____

5. _____

6. _____

7. _____

8. _____

9. _____

10. _____

11. _____

12. _____

13. _____

14. _____

15. _____

16. _____

17. _____

18. _____

19. _____

20. _____

21. _____

22. _____

23. _____

24. _____

25. _____

Using your words:

Choose at least ten words from your spelling list and write a silly story or poem using them.

Spelling Lesson:

As you hear them, write the spelling words for the day in the space provided. Be sure that you correct any words you have spelled incorrectly.

1. _____   14. _____

2. _____   15. _____

3. _____   16. _____

4. _____   17. _____

5. _____   18. _____

6. _____   19. _____

7. _____   20. _____

8. _____   21. _____

9. _____   22. _____

10. _____   23. _____

11. _____   24. _____

12. _____   25. _____

13. _____

Using your words:

Fill in the blanks with words from today's spelling list.

1. Don't ever be _____ to your teacher.

2. Which _____ is in Asia?

3. The police mounted a _____ sting operation.

4. Do not over _____ yourself.

5. We are having a cobbler for _____ .

6. He served as a _____ in the war.

7. We need a long sleeve _____ and a long _____ .

8. Do you have to go to _____ .

9. Do not _____ the glass. The water will pour out.

10. Paul became a _____ and sought to _____
    all of Rome.

Day 126

Spelling Lesson:

As you hear them, write the spelling words for the day in the space provided. Be sure that you correct any words you have spelled incorrectly.

1. _____

2. _____

3. _____

4. _____

5. _____

6. _____

7. _____

8. _____

9. _____

10. _____

11. _____

12. _____

13. _____

14. _____

15. _____

16. _____

17. _____

18. _____

19. _____

20. _____

21. _____

22. _____

23. _____

24. _____

25. _____

Using your words

List as many words as you can think of that have the following letters (in order) in them.

ert

Day 127

Spelling Lesson:

As you hear them, write the spelling words for the day in the space provided. Be sure that you correct any words you have spelled incorrectly.

1. _____

2. _____

3. _____

4. _____

5. _____

6. _____

7. _____

8. _____

9. _____

10. _____

11. _____

12. _____

13. _____

14. _____

15. _____

16. _____

17. _____

18. _____

19. _____

20. _____

21. _____

22. _____

23. _____

24. _____

25. _____

261

Using your words:

Unscramble these:

1. ohrsgut   _____

2. rdtrveee   _____

3. erxtvtroe   _____

4. itgesnnri   _____

5. loesrd   _____

6. erseoddcntci _____

7. trdeski   _____

8. usoyectr   _____

9. nbovctieerl   _____

10. edtriir   _____

Day 128

As you hear them, write the spelling words for the day in the space provided. Be sure that you correct any words you have spelled incorrectly.

1. _____

2. _____

3. _____

4. _____

5. _____

6. _____

7. _____

8. _____

9. _____

10. _____

11. _____

12. _____

13. _____

14. _____

15. _____

16. _____

17. _____

18. _____

19. _____

20. _____

21. _____

22. _____

23. _____

24. _____

25. _____

Using your words

Make as many words as you can from the following word.

convertibles

Day 129

Spelling Lesson:

As you hear them, write the spelling words for the day in the space provided. Be sure that you correct any words you have spelled incorrectly.

1. _____

2. _____

3. _____

4. _____

5. _____

6. _____

7. _____

8. _____

9. _____

10. _____

11. _____

12. _____

13. _____

14. _____

15. _____

16. _____

17. _____

18. _____

19. _____

20. _____

21. _____

22. _____

23. _____

24. _____

25. _____

Using your words:

Make as many words as you can with the following letters (in order) in them.

ert

ure

_____

_____

_____

_____

_____

_____

_____

_____

_____

_____

_____

_____

Sequential Spelling Level 5 - Student Workbook

Day 130

Spelling Lesson:

As you hear them, write the spelling words for the day in the space provided. Be sure that you correct any words you have spelled incorrectly.

1. _____

2. _____

3. _____

4. _____

5. _____

6. _____

7. _____

8. _____

9. _____

10. _____

11. _____

12. _____

13. _____

14. _____

15. _____

16. _____

17. _____

18. _____

19. _____

20. _____

21. _____

22. _____

23. _____

24. _____

25. _____

Using your words:

Unscramble these:

1. ursht   _____

2. lstuter   _____

3. frtuehr   _____

4. svastre   _____

5. ersplseau   _____

6. rueasmes   _____

7. amrlsev   _____

8. tlsretas   _____

9. slreoulymva _____

10. arssetvh   _____

Day 131

Spelling Lesson:

As you hear them, write the spelling words for the day in the space provided. Be sure that you correct any words you have spelled incorrectly.

1. _____

2. _____

3. _____

4. _____

5. _____

6. _____

7. _____

8. _____

9. _____

10. _____

11. _____

12. _____

13. _____

14. _____

15. _____

16. _____

17. _____

18. _____

19. _____

20. _____

21. _____

22. _____

23. _____

24. _____

25. _____

Using your words:

Fill in the blanks with words from today's spelling list.

1. All the fields have been _____ today.

2. We tripped and _____ into the door.

3. In the race, we _____ all the obstacles.

4. Is that cut _____ you?

5. The refugees _____ for 30 days until help arrived and ended their

   _____.

6. The loud noise _____ us!

7. Get the payment from the _____.

8. Please take a careful _____ of the beam.

9. The _____ _____ a small statue.

Spelling Lesson:

As you hear them, write the spelling words for the day in the space provided. Be sure that you correct any words you have spelled incorrectly.

1. _____

2. _____

3. _____

4. _____

5. _____

6. _____

7. _____

8. _____

9. _____

10. _____

11. _____

12. _____

13. _____

14. _____

15. _____

16. _____

17. _____

18. _____

19. _____

20. _____

21. _____

22. _____

23. _____

24. _____

25. _____

Using your words

```
H   U   R   T   L   I   N   G   A   W   G   M   J   T   G   B   B   E
C   C   X   P   V   K   V   Z   D   X   G   E   V   R   H   H   F   K
W   O   O   D   C   A   R   V   I   N   G   A   M   E   A   U   A   Z
K   M   Q   F   Z   E   H   N   C   R   V   S   E   A   R   R   R   G
X   F   G   C   A   R   V   I   N   G   I   U   A   S   V   D   T   X
F   A   R   T   H   R   I   T   I   S   H   R   S   U   E   L   H   J
T   R   E   A   S   U   R   E   R   S   C   E   U   R   S   I   E   N
J   D   C   U   Y   W   N   U   F   V   K   M   R   Y   T   N   S   H
I   S   T   A   R   T   L   I   N   G   Y   E   I   Z   I   G   T   C
M   L   L   J   I   V   M   E   M   G   T   N   N   C   N   P   O   R
P   S   S   E   W   N   W   Z   O   O   V   T   G   V   G   H   Z   Q
F   U   R   T   H   E   S   T   C   D   J   S   Q   W   L   W   Z   D
```

Find the following words in the puzzle.
Words are hidden → ↓ and ↘ .

ARTHRITIS   HURDLING   STARTLING
CARVING   HURTLING   TREASURERS
FARTHEST   MEASUREMENTS   TREASURY
FURTHEST   MEASURING   WOODCARVING
HARVESTING   SEWN

Day 133

As you hear them, write the spelling words for the day in the space provided. Be sure that you correct any words you have spelled incorrectly.

1. _____

2. _____

3. _____

4. _____

5. _____

6. _____

7. _____

8. _____

9. _____

10. _____

11. _____

12. _____

13. _____

14. _____

15. _____

16. _____

17. _____

18. _____

19. _____

20. _____

21. _____

22. _____

23. _____

24. _____

25. _____

Using your words:

List as many words as you can with the following letters (in order) in them.

ars

eas

Day 134

As you hear them, write the spelling words for the day in the space provided. Be sure that you correct any words you have spelled incorrectly.

1. _____

2. _____

3. _____

4. _____

5. _____

6. _____

7. _____

8. _____

9. _____

10. _____

11. _____

12. _____

13. _____

14. _____

15. _____

16. _____

17. _____

18. _____

19. _____

20. _____

21. _____

22. _____

23. _____

24. _____

25. _____

Using your words:

Choose ten of today's spelling words and use them in a paragraph, silly story or poem.

_____

_____

_____

_____

_____

_____

_____

_____

_____

_____

Day 135

As you hear them, write the spelling words for the day in the space provided. Be sure that you correct any words you have spelled incorrectly.

1. _____

2. _____

3. _____

4. _____

5. _____

6. _____

7. _____

8. _____

9. _____

10. _____

11. _____

12. _____

13. _____

14. _____

15. _____

16. _____

17. _____

18. _____

19. _____

20. _____

21. _____

22. _____

23. _____

24. _____

25. _____

Using your words:

Fill in the blanks with words from today's spelling list.

1. The soup needs more _____.

2. Your efforts have been _____!

3. The _____ was transported to the cemetary.

4. How was that sentence_____?

5. The angry man was not _____ by our apology.

6. That house has already been _____.

7. It might, however, be available to be_____.

8. We _____ out of the driveway and into the road.

9. The weather is most _____ for late fall.

10. You are my son with whom I am most _____.

Spelling Lesson:

As you hear them, write the spelling words for the day in the space provided. Be sure that you correct any words you have spelled incorrectly.

1. _____

2. _____

3. _____

4. _____

5. _____

6. _____

7. _____

8. _____

9. _____

10. _____

11. _____

12. _____

13. _____

14. _____

15. _____

16. _____

17. _____

18. _____

19. _____

20. _____

21. _____

22. _____

23. _____

24. _____

25. _____

Using your words:

Choose at least ten words from your spelling list and use each in a sentence.

1._____

_____

2._____

_____

3._____

_____

4._____

_____

5._____

_____

6._____

_____

7._____

_____

8._____

_____

9._____

_____

10._____

_____

Day 137

As you hear them, write the spelling words for the day in the space provided. Be sure that you correct any words you have spelled incorrectly.

1. _____

2. _____

3. _____

4. _____

5. _____

6. _____

7. _____

8. _____

9. _____

10. _____

11. _____

12. _____

13. _____

14. _____

15. _____

16. _____

17. _____

18. _____

19. _____

20. _____

21. _____

22. _____

23. _____

24. _____

25. _____

Using your words:

Choose ten of today's spelling words and use them in a paragraph, silly story or poem.

Spelling Lesson:

As you hear them, write the spelling words for the day in the space provided. Be sure that you correct any words you have spelled incorrectly.

1. _____

2. _____

3. _____

4. _____

5. _____

6. _____

7. _____

8. _____

9. _____

10. _____

11. _____

12. _____

13. _____

14. _____

15. _____

16. _____

17. _____

18. _____

19. _____

20. _____

21. _____

22. _____

23. _____

24. _____

25. _____

Using your words:

List as many words as you can that have the following letters (in order) in them.

ose

_____

_____

_____

_____

_____

_____

_____

_____

_____

Day 139

As you hear them, write the spelling words for the day in the space provided. Be sure that you correct any words you have spelled incorrectly.

1. _____

2. _____

3. _____

4. _____

5. _____

6. _____

7. _____

8. _____

9. _____

10. _____

11. _____

12. _____

13. _____

14. _____

15. _____

16. _____

17. _____

18. _____

19. _____

20. _____

21. _____

22. _____

23. _____

24. _____

25. _____

Using your words:

Unscramble these:

1. raolutgP   _____

2. icdseoe   _____

3. ostsloe   _____

4. saeoocb   _____

5. fsrgoiecoln_____

6. olenedos   _____

7. nyso   _____

8. ncgnsleio   _____

9. pcioled   _____

10. eldothc   _____

Spelling Lesson:

As you hear them, write the spelling words for the day in the space provided. Be sure that you correct any words you have spelled incorrectly.

1. _____

2. _____

3. _____

4. _____

5. _____

6. _____

7. _____

8. _____

9. _____

10. _____

11. _____

12. _____

13. _____

14. _____

15. _____

16. _____

17. _____

18. _____

19. _____

20. _____

21. _____

22. _____

23. _____

24. _____

25. _____

Using your words:

Choose at least ten words from your spelling list and use them in a short paragraph, silly story or poem.

Day 141

As you hear them, write the spelling words for the day in the space provided. Be sure that you correct any words you have spelled incorrectly.

1. _____

2. _____

3. _____

4. _____

5. _____

6. _____

7. _____

8. _____

9. _____

10. _____

11. _____

12. _____

13. _____

14. _____

15. _____

16. _____

17. _____

18. _____

19. _____

20. _____

21. _____

22. _____

23. _____

24. _____

25. _____

Using your words:

Fill in the blanks with words from today's spelling list.

1. Pardon me! I don't mean to _____ .

2. Did the man _____ marriage to her?.

3. Some countries can be quite _____ .

4. Does it _____ you to watch movies?

5. Do you _____ we could _____ the game?

6. We will _____ your effort to change the neighborhood.

7. How does the _____ get started with the app?

8. Do you know where _____ ?

9. Christmas is _____ now. I can't wait!.

10. I was afraid to hear the _____ .

Day 142

Spelling Lesson:

As you hear them, write the spelling words for the day in the space provided. Be sure that you correct any words you have spelled incorrectly.

1. _____
2. _____
3. _____
4. _____
5. _____
6. _____
7. _____
8. _____
9. _____
10. _____
11. _____
12. _____
13. _____

14. _____
15. _____
16. _____
17. _____
18. _____
19. _____
20. _____
21. _____
22. _____
23. _____
24. _____
25. _____

Using your words:

Unscramble these

1. spspoeus   _____

2. mecpoddeso _____

3. poresdpo   _____

4. meorso   _____

5. leusocg   _____

6. leoss   _____

7. uaesms   _____

8. oentdrsaps _____

9. slcoyel   _____

10. ansedsgio   _____

Spelling Lesson:

As you hear them, write the spelling words for the day in the space provided. Be sure that you correct any words you have spelled incorrectly.

1. _____

2. _____

3. _____

4. _____

5. _____

6. _____

7. _____

8. _____

9. _____

10. _____

11. _____

12. _____

13. _____

14. _____

15. _____

16. _____

17. _____

18. _____

19. _____

20. _____

21. _____

22. _____

23. _____

24. _____

25. _____

Using your words:

Make as many words as you can from the following word.

decomposing

Spelling Lesson:

As you hear them, write the spelling words for the day in the space provided. Be sure that you correct any words you have spelled incorrectly.

1. _____

2. _____

3. _____

4. _____

5. _____

6. _____

7. _____

8. _____

9. _____

10. _____

11. _____

12. _____

13. _____

14. _____

15. _____

16. _____

17. _____

18. _____

19. _____

20. _____

21. _____

22. _____

23. _____

24. _____

25. _____

Using your words:

Can you  the words?

```
Q  Q  Y  E  X  Z  E  U  P  O  S  I  T  I  O  N  Z  P
J  M  N  X  I  J  H  K  S  H  M  A  C  H  E  T  E  R
I  Y  I  Y  F  D  O  S  A  G  E  O  X  T  Y  W  U  O
S  U  P  P  O  S  I  T  I  O  N  I  P  J  G  Q  F  P
L  L  O  P  P  O  S  I  T  I  O  N  W  X  Z  Q  B  O
W  Q  Z  L  L  U  S  M  A  J  V  E  R  B  O  S  E  S
Q  K  X  T  R  A  N  S  P  O  S  I  T  I  O  N  N  I
J  E  I  Q  C  M  G  Z  P  A  M  U  S  I  N  G  I  T
W  I  P  E  O  X  Y  M  J  U  L  O  S  I  N  G  D  I
C  Q  J  O  C  O  S  E  L  G  N  P  G  N  A  O  I  O
X  Y  X  D  U  S  A  G  E  F  C  L  O  S  E  S  T  N
E  X  P  O  S  I  T  I  O  N  W  Y  O  L  K  Y  V  U
```

Find the following words in the puzzle.
Words are hidden → ↓ and ↘ .

AMUSING	LOSING	SUPPOSITION
CLOSEST	MACHETE	TRANSPOSITION
DOSAGE	OPPOSITION	USAGE
EXPOSITION	POSITION	VERBOSE
JOCOSE	PROPOSITION	

Spelling Lesson:

As you hear them, write the spelling words for the day in the space provided. Be sure that you correct any words you have spelled incorrectly.

1. _____

2. _____

3. _____

4. _____

5. _____

6. _____

7. _____

8. _____

9. _____

10. _____

11. _____

12. _____

13. _____

14. _____

15. _____

16. _____

17. _____

18. _____

19. _____

20. _____

21. _____

22. _____

23. _____

24. _____

25. _____

Using your words:

List as many words as possible with the following letters (in order) in them.

use

_____

_____

_____

_____

_____

_____

_____

_____

_____

_____

Day 146

Spelling Lesson:

As you hear them, write the spelling words for the day in the space provided. Be sure that you correct any words you have spelled incorrectly.

1. _____

2. _____

3. _____

4. _____

5. _____

6. _____

7. _____

8. _____

9. _____

10. _____

11. _____

12. _____

13. _____

14. _____

15. _____

16. _____

17. _____

18. _____

19. _____

20. _____

21. _____

22. _____

23. _____

24. _____

25. _____

Using your words:

Fill in the blanks with words from today's spelling list.

1. Elephants often have long _____.

2. Everyone _____ to eat the liver.

3. The thief had many _____.

4. I have a scary mask for _____ .

5. I got a little _____ when I put on weight.

6. The light _____ through the treetops.

7. The soldiers use _____ to fool the enemy.

8. Some of the people in northern Spain are _____ .

9. We need the pause that _____ .

10. Throw the corn _____ in the garbage.

Spelling Lesson:

As you hear them, write the spelling words for the day in the space provided. Be sure that you correct any words you have spelled incorrectly.

1. _____   14. _____

2. _____   15. _____

3. _____   16. _____

4. _____   17. _____

5. _____   18. _____

6. _____   19. _____

7. _____   20. _____

8. _____   21. _____

9. _____   22. _____

10. _____   23. _____

11. _____   24. _____

12. _____   25. _____

13. _____

Using your words:

Make as many words as you can from the following word.

refreshment

Day 148

Spelling Lesson:

As you hear them, write the spelling words for the day in the space provided. Be sure that you correct any words you have spelled incorrectly.

1. _____

2. _____

3. _____

4. _____

5. _____

6. _____

7. _____

8. _____

9. _____

10. _____

11. _____

12. _____

13. _____

14. _____

15. _____

16. _____

17. _____

18. _____

19. _____

20. _____

21. _____

22. _____

23. _____

24. _____

25. _____

Using your words:

Choose at least ten words from your spelling list and use them in a short paragraph, silly story or poem.

Day 149

Spelling Lesson:

As you hear them, write the spelling words for the day in the space provided. Be sure that you correct any words you have spelled incorrectly.

1. _____

2. _____

3. _____

4. _____

5. _____

6. _____

7. _____

8. _____

9. _____

10. _____

11. _____

12. _____

13. _____

14. _____

15. _____

16. _____

17. _____

18. _____

19. _____

20. _____

21. _____

22. _____

23. _____

24. _____

25. _____

Using your words:

Use each of these words correctly in a sentence.

1. asp_____

_____

2. rasp_____

_____

3. vesper_____

_____

4. wisp_____

_____

5. prosperous_____

_____

6. canvasses_____

_____

7. harass_____

_____

8. waste_____

_____

9. waist_____

_____

10. baste_____

_____

Day 150

Spelling Lesson:

As you hear them, write the spelling words for the day in the space provided. Be sure that you correct any words you have spelled incorrectly.

1. _____

2. _____

3. _____

4. _____

5. _____

6. _____

7. _____

8. _____

9. _____

10. _____

11. _____

12. _____

13. _____

14. _____

15. _____

16. _____

17. _____

18. _____

19. _____

20. _____

21. _____

22. _____

23. _____

24. _____

25. _____

Using your words:

List as many words as possible with the following letters (in order) in them.

asp

ass

_____

_____

_____

_____

_____

_____

_____

_____

_____

_____

Day 151

Spelling Lesson:

As you hear them, write the spelling words for the day in the space provided. Be sure that you correct any words you have spelled incorrectly.

1. _____

2. _____

3. _____

4. _____

5. _____

6. _____

7. _____

8. _____

9. _____

10. _____

11. _____

12. _____

13. _____

14. _____

15. _____

16. _____

17. _____

18. _____

19. _____

20. _____

21. _____

22. _____

23. _____

24. _____

25. _____

Using your words:

Unscramble these:

1. dpsgae _____

2. eapclsd _____

3. pglose _____

4. potsiepryr _____

5. epsnmcaesso _____

6. sdrearembas _____

7. sopedrerp _____

8. rahsdeas _____

9. lwuatfes _____

10. daepst _____

Day 152

Spelling Lesson:

As you hear them, write the spelling words for the day in the space provided. Be sure that you correct any words you have spelled incorrectly.

1. _____

2. _____

3. _____

4. _____

5. _____

6. _____

7. _____

8. _____

9. _____

10. _____

11. _____

12. _____

13. _____

14. _____

15. _____

16. _____

17. _____

18. _____

19. _____

20. _____

21. _____

22. _____

23. _____

24. _____

25. _____

Using your words:

Choose at least ten words from your spelling list and use them in a short paragraph, silly story or poem.

Day 153

Spelling Lesson:

As you hear them, write the spelling words for the day in the space provided. Be sure that you correct any words you have spelled incorrectly.

1. _____

2. _____

3. _____

4. _____

5. _____

6. _____

7. _____

8. _____

9. _____

10. _____

11. _____

12. _____

13. _____

14. _____

15. _____

16. _____

17. _____

18. _____

19. _____

20. _____

21. _____

22. _____

23. _____

24. _____

25. _____

Using your words:

Sound-alike words:

cast/caste
plate/plait
straight/strait

Use a dictionary to find the meanings of the words you
don't know. Then use each of them correctly in a sentence.

1._____

_____

2._____

_____

3._____

_____

4._____

_____

5._____

_____

6._____

_____

Spelling Lesson:

As you hear them, write the spelling words for the day in the space provided. Be sure that you correct any words you have spelled incorrectly.

1. _____   14. _____

2. _____   15. _____

3. _____   16. _____

4. _____   17. _____

5. _____   18. _____

6. _____   19. _____

7. _____   20. _____

8. _____   21. _____

9. _____   22. _____

10. _____   23. _____

11. _____   24. _____

12. _____   25. _____

13. _____

Using your words:

List as many words as you can that have the following letters (in order) in them.

ast

ait

Day 155

Spelling Lesson:

As you hear them, write the spelling words for the day in the space provided. Be sure that you correct any words you have spelled incorrectly.

1. _____

2. _____

3. _____

4. _____

5. _____

6. _____

7. _____

8. _____

9. _____

10. _____

11. _____

12. _____

13. _____

14. _____

15. _____

16. _____

17. _____

18. _____

19. _____

20. _____

21. _____

22. _____

23. _____

24. _____

25. _____

Using your words:

Unscramble these:

1. mlaabsetd   _____

2. hanedset   _____

3. etstad   _____

4. vaetxuhise   _____

5. utiaccs   _____

6. ifetsy   _____

7. rpttoiar   _____

8. ilaedtp   _____

9. agdetehruls _____

10. ealuhdg   _____

Day 156

As you hear them, write the spelling words for the day in the space provided. Be sure that you correct any words you have spelled incorrectly.

1. _____

2. _____

3. _____

4. _____

5. _____

6. _____

7. _____

8. _____

9. _____

10. _____

11. _____

12. _____

13. _____

14. _____

15. _____

16. _____

17. _____

18. _____

19. _____

20. _____

21. _____

22. _____

23. _____

24. _____

25. _____

319

Using your words:

Can you (find) the words?

```
O  B  A  I  T  I  N  G  X  M  P  D  R  E  W  S  N  V
C  G  E  G  V  L  Q  F  W  B  N  K  O  H  R  M  A  F
T  H  P  M  U  Z  A  B  E  A  W  C  W  X  J  T  U  G
W  A  I  S  T  K  O  U  T  I  S  A  J  P  S  C  G  S
K  X  U  A  M  C  O  Y  G  A  S  T  I  U  S  C  H  S
V  B  U  T  H  A  S  T  Y  H  S  T  E  T  Z  K  T  Y
U  D  F  L  N  K  C  O  B  G  I  T  I  F  I  B  Y  M
G  L  A  M  B  A  S  T  I  N  G  N  I  E  U  N  N  T
F  C  A  U  S  T  I  C  A  L  L  Y  G  N  S  L  G  M
U  H  M  J  B  L  M  B  H  G  H  R  T  X  G  T  U  N
A  E  V  M  T  H  O  U  G  H  T  H  T  F  I  B  S  O
R  B  N  G  A  I  T  J  Z  O  H  N  O  X  T  O  B  T
```

Find the following words in the puzzle.
Words are hidden → ↓ and ↘ .

BAITING	LAMBASTING	THOUGHT
CAUSTICALLY	LAUGHING	WAIST
FEISTIEST	NAUGHTY	WAITING
GAIT	TASTING	WASTEFUL
HASTY	TAUT	

Sequential Spelling Level 5 - Student Workbook

Day 157

Spelling Lesson:

As you hear them, write the spelling words for the day in the space provided. Be sure that you correct any words you have spelled incorrectly.

1. _____

2. _____

3. _____

4. _____

5. _____

6. _____

7. _____

8. _____

9. _____

10. _____

11. _____

12. _____

13. _____

14. _____

15. _____

16. _____

17. _____

18. _____

19. _____

20. _____

21. _____

22. _____

23. _____

24. _____

25. _____

321

Using your words:

Sound-alike words

mete/meat
route/rout

Use a dictionary to find the meanings of the words you don't know. Write them in sentences with other words on your spelling list.

1._____

_____

2._____

_____

3._____

_____

4._____

_____

Spelling Lesson:

As you hear them, write the spelling words for the day in the space provided. Be sure that you correct any words you have spelled incorrectly.

1. _____

2. _____

3. _____

4. _____

5. _____

6. _____

7. _____

8. _____

9. _____

10. _____

11. _____

12. _____

13. _____

14. _____

15. _____

16. _____

17. _____

18. _____

19. _____

20. _____

21. _____

22. _____

23. _____

24. _____

25. _____

Using your words:

List as many words as you can that have the following letters (in order) in them.

ete

Day 159

Spelling Lesson:

As you hear them, write the spelling words for the day in the space provided. Be sure that you correct any words you have spelled incorrectly.

1. _____

2. _____

3. _____

4. _____

5. _____

6. _____

7. _____

8. _____

9. _____

10. _____

11. _____

12. _____

13. _____

14. _____

15. _____

16. _____

17. _____

18. _____

19. _____

20. _____

21. _____

22. _____

23. _____

24. _____

25. _____

Using your words:

Fill in the blanks with words from today's spelling list.

1. We left the party _____ so nobody noticed.

2. The word_____ is short for _____.

3. We _____ our match.

4. He is a very _____ _____.

5. The judge _____ out a heavy sentence for the crime.

6. We _____ all the computer files.

7. By what _____ do you determine victory?

8. We asked the _____ for his boss' telephone number.

9. The _____ was caught with the false bills.

10. We _____ the mail to the proper place.

Day 160

Spelling Lesson:

As you hear them, write the spelling words for the day in the space provided. Be sure that you correct any words you have spelled incorrectly.

1. _____

2. _____

3. _____

4. _____

5. _____

6. _____

7. _____

8. _____

9. _____

10. _____

11. _____

12. _____

13. _____

14. _____

15. _____

16. _____

17. _____

18. _____

19. _____

20. _____

21. _____

22. _____

23. _____

24. _____

25. _____

327

Using your words:

Choose at least ten words from your spelling list and use them in a short paragraph, silly story or poem.

_____

_____

_____

_____

_____

_____

_____

_____

_____

_____

_____

Evaluation Test #4

Fill in the blanks with the missing letters.

1. A judge is supposed to be imp_____.

2. Tomorrow will not be my twenty-f_____ birthday.

3. I love driving a con_____.

4. I do expect common c_____ from all of you.

5. Millions of people have died from st_____.

6. A tailor must be accurate with m_____.

7. The traitor was arrested, tried, and convicted of tr_____.

8. Everybody likes to be pr_____ once in a while.

9. Have you ever tried to read any insurance p_____ ?

10. You should l_____ up your muscles before exercising.

11. Have you ever met your opp_____ before today?

12. That was a rather am_____ story.

13. I enjoy having refr_____ after playing golf.

14. Have you ever been to a m_____ ball?

15. Don't you hate to be embarr_____?

16. It's w_____ to throw away perfectly good clothes.

17. Our team had been sl_____.

18. I'm not just tired. I'm exh_____.

19. I enjoy all sports. I love comp_____.

20. I also enjoy athl_____.

Day 161

Spelling Lesson:

As you hear them, write the spelling words for the day in the space provided. Be sure that you correct any words you have spelled incorrectly.

1. _____

2. _____

3. _____

4. _____

5. _____

6. _____

7. _____

8. _____

9. _____

10. _____

11. _____

12. _____

13. _____

14. _____

15. _____

16. _____

17. _____

18. _____

19. _____

20. _____

21. _____

22. _____

23. _____

24. _____

25. _____

Using your words:

List as many words as you can that have the following letters (in order) in them.

ute

Day 162

As you hear them, write the spelling words for the day in the space provided. Be sure that you correct any words you have spelled incorrectly.

1. _____

2. _____

3. _____

4. _____

5. _____

6. _____

7. _____

8. _____

9. _____

10. _____

11. _____

12. _____

13. _____

14. _____

15. _____

16. _____

17. _____

18. _____

19. _____

20. _____

21. _____

22. _____

23. _____

24. _____

25. _____

Using your words:

Fill in the blanks with words from today's spelling list.

1. The country _____ its veterans.

2. Did the soldiers jump with _____?

3. Please come _____!

4. You must not treat anyone _____.

5. An oil spill _____ a waterway.

6. We have _____ a new policy.

7. How many _____ until we leave?

8. I am _____ exhausted!

9. Ice melts and _____ your drink.

10. What _____ a good life?

Day 163

As you hear them, write the spelling words for the day in the space provided. Be sure that you correct any words you have spelled incorrectly.

1. _____

2. _____

3. _____

4. _____

5. _____

6. _____

7. _____

8. _____

9. _____

10. _____

11. _____

12. _____

13. _____

14. _____

15. _____

16. _____

17. _____

18. _____

19. _____

20. _____

21. _____

22. _____

23. _____

24. _____

25. _____

Using your words:

Unscramble these:

1 dtooel   _____

2. ptlorelu   _____

3. oulseetr   _____

4. cuoninittost _____

5. diutttesusb _____

6. tuyialrtb   _____

7. nheefthocr _____

8. teattus   _____

9. ieusrht   _____

10. tueedstti   _____

Sequential Spelling Level 5 - Student Workbook

Day 164

Spelling Lesson:

As you hear them, write the spelling words for the day in the space provided. Be sure that you correct any words you have spelled incorrectly.

1. _____

2. _____

3. _____

4. _____

5. _____

6. _____

7. _____

8. _____

9. _____

10. _____

11. _____

12. _____

13. _____

14. _____

15. _____

16. _____

17. _____

18. _____

19. _____

20. _____

21. _____

22. _____

23. _____

24. _____

25. _____

Using your words:

Write a sentence using the following words:

1. looting _____

_____.

2. diluting _____

_____.

3. resolution _____

_____.

4. institutional_____

_____.

5. unconstitutional_____

_____.

6. substitution_____

_____.

7. destitution _____

_____.

8.restitution_____

_____.

9.statutes_____

_____.

10.come forth_____

_____.

Day 165

As you hear them, write the spelling words for the day in the space provided. Be sure that you correct any words you have spelled incorrectly.

1. _____

2. _____

3. _____

4. _____

5. _____

6. _____

7. _____

8. _____

9. _____

10. _____

11. _____

12. _____

13. _____

14. _____

15. _____

16. _____

17. _____

18. _____

19. _____

20. _____

21. _____

22. _____

23. _____

24. _____

25. _____

Using your words:

Choose ten of today's spelling words and use them in a paragraph, silly story or poem.

Day 166

As you hear them, write the spelling words for the day in the space provided. Be sure that you correct any words you have spelled incorrectly.

1. _____

2. _____

3. _____

4. _____

5. _____

6. _____

7. _____

8. _____

9. _____

10. _____

11. _____

12. _____

13. _____

14. _____

15. _____

16. _____

17. _____

18. _____

19. _____

20. _____

21. _____

22. _____

23. _____

24. _____

25. _____

Using your words:

List as many words as you can that have the following letters (in order) in them.

ute

_____

_____

_____

_____

_____

_____

_____

_____

_____

_____

Spelling Lesson:

As you hear them, write the spelling words for the day in the space provided. Be sure that you correct any words you have spelled incorrectly.

1. _____

2. _____

3. _____

4. _____

5. _____

6. _____

7. _____

8. _____

9. _____

10. _____

11. _____

12. _____

13. _____

14. _____

15. _____

16. _____

17. _____

18. _____

19. _____

20. _____

21. _____

22. _____

23. _____

24. _____

25. _____

Using your words:

Use a dictionary to find the definitions of the words you don't know. Use each of these in a sentence.

1. acutely_____

_____

2. persecuted_____

_____

3. prosecutor_____

_____

4. electrocuted_____

_____

5. tributary_____

_____

6. refuting_____

_____

7. reputing_____

_____

8. myths_____

_____

Day 168

Spelling Lesson:

As you hear them, write the spelling words for the day in the space provided. Be sure that you correct any words you have spelled incorrectly.

1. _____

2. _____

3. _____

4. _____

5. _____

6. _____

7. _____

8. _____

9. _____

10. _____

11. _____

12. _____

13. _____

14. _____

15. _____

16. _____

17. _____

18. _____

19. _____

20. _____

21. _____

22. _____

23. _____

24. _____

25. _____

Using your words:

Can you find the words?

```
P   C   S   S   C   D   S   N   U   J   R   U   C   L   Y   R   B   R
E   G   O   P   G   U   U   C   P   G   D   I   O   Q   E   E   N   X
R   O   O   M   G   D   E   P   T   H   S   S   N   J   A   F   U   Z
S   T   S   P   M   O   N   T   H   S   V   D   T   F   R   U   R   M
E   P   E   R   M   U   T   A   T   I   O   N   R   I   T   T   R   U
C   I   B   Z   W   H   T   O   F   P   E   K   I   L   H   A   I   T
U   F   P   V   N   L   P   A   J   R   Q   X   B   T   P   T   Y   A
T   Q   U   R   Y   I   R   C   T   Z   O   E   U   H   I   I   B   T
I   M   Y   T   H   I   C   A   L   I   H   L   T   Y   C   O   X   I
O   B   Z   S   A   C   U   I   T   Y   O   F   I   D   E   N   B   O
N   R   E   P   U   T   A   T   I   O   N   N   O   R   C   R   U   N
R   K   M   Y   T   H   O   L   O   G   Y   O   N   W   S   V   K   G
```

Find the following words in the puzzle.
Words are hidden → ↓ and ↘ .

ACUITY
COMMUTATION
CONTRIBUTION
DEPTHS
EARTH

FILTHY
MONTHS
MUTATION
MYTHICAL
MYTHOLOGY

PERMUTATION
PERSECUTION
REFUTATION
REPUTATION

Spelling Lesson:

As you hear them, write the spelling words for the day in the space provided. Be sure that you correct any words you have spelled incorrectly.

1. _____

2. _____

3. _____

4. _____

5. _____

6. _____

7. _____

8. _____

9. _____

10. _____

11. _____

12. _____

13. _____

14. _____

15. _____

16. _____

17. _____

18. _____

19. _____

20. _____

21. _____

22. _____

23. _____

24. _____

25. _____

Using your words:

Fill in the blanks with words from today's spelling list.

1. We all gather around the _____ .

2. We answered a lengthy _____ .

3. I am _____ to _____ anyone.

4. You are dirty. You really need to _____.

5. This _____ can be used to _____ the needy.

6. We took a solemn _____ to serve and protect.

7. I want to know the _____!

8. Our country knew a _____ in freedom.

9. What is your _____?

10. We got the top _____ on the train.

Day 170

As you hear them, write the spelling words for the day in the space provided. Be sure that you correct any words you have spelled incorrectly.

1. _____

2. _____

3. _____

4. _____

5. _____

6. _____

7. _____

8. _____

9. _____

10. _____

11. _____

12. _____

13. _____

14. _____

15. _____

16. _____

17. _____

18. _____

19. _____

20. _____

21. _____

22. _____

23. _____

24. _____

25. _____

Using your words:

Unscramble these:

1   srhetha   _____

2. owhgrt   _____

3. altsoeohm   _____

4. scthleo   _____

5. utosnesqi   _____

6. otseinsgusg   _____

7. oistnmo   _____

8. omonrpsoit   _____

9. otsnoni   _____

10. ebhsat   _____

Day 171

Spelling Lesson:

As you hear them, write the spelling words for the day in the space provided. Be sure that you correct any words you have spelled incorrectly.

1. _____

2. _____

3. _____

4. _____

5. _____

6. _____

7. _____

8. _____

9. _____

10. _____

11. _____

12. _____

13. _____

14. _____

15. _____

16. _____

17. _____

18. _____

19. _____

20. _____

21. _____

22. _____

23. _____

24. _____

25. _____

Using your words:

Make as many words as you can from the following word.

questionable

Day 172

As you hear them, write the spelling words for the day in the space provided. Be sure that you correct any words you have spelled incorrectly.

1. _____

2. _____

3. _____

4. _____

5. _____

6. _____

7. _____

8. _____

9. _____

10. _____

11. _____

12. _____

13. _____

14. _____

15. _____

16. _____

17. _____

18. _____

19. _____

20. _____

21. _____

22. _____

23. _____

24. _____

25. _____

Using your words:

Choose at least ten words from your spelling list and use them in a short paragraph, silly story or poem.

_____

_____

_____

_____

_____

_____

_____

_____

_____

_____

Spelling Lesson:

As you hear them, write the spelling words for the day in the space provided. Be sure that you correct any words you have spelled incorrectly.

1. _____

2. _____

3. _____

4. _____

5. _____

6. _____

7. _____

8. _____

9. _____

10. _____

11. _____

12. _____

13. _____

14. _____

15. _____

16. _____

17. _____

18. _____

19. _____

20. _____

21. _____

22. _____

23. _____

24. _____

25. _____

Using your words:

List as many words as you can that have the following letters (in order) in them.

et

_____

_____

_____

_____

_____

_____

_____

_____

_____

_____

Spelling Lesson:

As you hear them, write the spelling words for the day in the space provided. Be sure that you correct any words you have spelled incorrectly.

1. _____

2. _____

3. _____

4. _____

5. _____

6. _____

7. _____

8. _____

9. _____

10. _____

11. _____

12. _____

13. _____

14. _____

15. _____

16. _____

17. _____

18. _____

19. _____

20. _____

21. _____

22. _____

23. _____

24. _____

25. _____

Using your words:

Use each of these words correctly in a sentence.

1. buffets/buffets_____

_____

2. dietician_____

_____

3. comets_____

_____

4. bonnets_____

_____

5. interprets_____

_____

6. garrets_____

_____

7. rackets_____

_____

8. racquets_____

_____

9. rivets_____

_____

10. tappets_____

_____

Day 175

As you hear them, write the spelling words for the day in the space provided. Be sure that you correct any words you have spelled incorrectly.

1. _____

2. _____

3. _____

4. _____

5. _____

6. _____

7. _____

8. _____

9. _____

10. _____

11. _____

12. _____

13. _____

14. _____

15. _____

16. _____

17. _____

18. _____

19. _____

20. _____

21. _____

22. _____

23. _____

24. _____

25. _____

Using your words:

Unscramble these:

1. tgmaenic _____

2. rynlepaat _____

3. itieanscdi _____

4. aceltn _____

5. tretru _____

6. aecertker _____

7. slecsot _____

8. apcreted _____

9. btianryec _____

10. irutqee _____

Day 176

Spelling Lesson:

As you hear them, write the spelling words for the day in the space provided. Be sure that you correct any words you have spelled incorrectly.

1. _____

2. _____

3. _____

4. _____

5. _____

6. _____

7. _____

8. _____

9. _____

10. _____

11. _____

12. _____

13. _____

14. _____

15. _____

16. _____

17. _____

18. _____

19. _____

20. _____

21. _____

22. _____

23. _____

24. _____

25. _____

Using your words:

Can you find the words?

```
X  N  P  L  A  N  E  T  A  R  I  U  M  U  O  O  N  F
M  S  G  Z  B  N  T  R  I  V  E  T  S  W  J  I  W  X
P  O  E  T  I  C  M  A  G  N  E  T  I  S  M  S  A  E
C  G  F  O  S  O  N  N  E  T  S  M  V  Y  J  U  C  C
G  L  A  N  C  E  T  S  B  W  W  O  Q  R  D  E  A  D
P  S  E  V  E  G  R  O  M  M  E  T  S  A  F  T  M  T
J  I  R  E  T  G  J  Z  T  K  T  U  R  R  E  T  S  Q
M  I  S  I  N  T  E  R  P  R  E  T  A  T  I  O  N  C
S  J  B  U  F  F  E  T  I  N  G  V  X  F  R  E  S  Q
S  S  J  S  P  I  N  E  T  S  D  P  R  L  P  C  J  X
W  F  C  Q  U  I  E  T  E  S  T  G  Y  V  C  O  Y  A
J  I  A  L  M  D  G  U  S  S  E  T  S  L  J  F  P  R
```

Find the following words in the puzzle.
Words are hidden → ↓ and ↘ .

BUFFETING
GROMMETS
GUSSETS
LANCETS
MAGNETISM

MISINTERPRETATION
PLANETARIUM
POETIC
QUIETEST
SONNETS

SPINETS
SUET
TRIVETS
TURRETS

Spelling Lesson:

As you hear them, write the spelling words for the day in the space provided. Be sure that you correct any words you have spelled incorrectly.

1. _____

2. _____

3. _____

4. _____

5. _____

6. _____

7. _____

8. _____

9. _____

10. _____

11. _____

12. _____

13. _____

14. _____

15. _____

16. _____

17. _____

18. _____

19. _____

20. _____

21. _____

22. _____

23. _____

24. _____

25. _____

Using your words:

Choose ten of today's spelling words and use them in a paragraph, silly story or poem.

_____

_____

_____

_____

_____

_____

_____

_____

_____

_____

Day 178

Spelling Lesson:

As you hear them, write the spelling words for the day in the space provided. Be sure that you correct any words you have spelled incorrectly.

1. _____

2. _____

3. _____

4. _____

5. _____

6. _____

7. _____

8. _____

9. _____

10. _____

11. _____

12. _____

13. _____

14. _____

15. _____

16. _____

17. _____

18. _____

19. _____

20. _____

21. _____

22. _____

23. _____

24. _____

25. _____

Using your words:

List as many words as you can that have the following letters (in order) in them

it

_____

_____

_____

_____

_____

_____

_____

_____

_____

_____

_____

_____

_____

Day 179

As you hear them, write the spelling words for the day in the space provided. Be sure that you correct any words you have spelled incorrectly.

1. _____

2. _____

3. _____

4. _____

5. _____

6. _____

7. _____

8. _____

9. _____

10. _____

11. _____

12. _____

13. _____

14. _____

15. _____

16. _____

17. _____

18. _____

19. _____

20. _____

21. _____

22. _____

23. _____

24. _____

25. _____

Using your words

Fill in the blanks with words from today's spelling list.

1. The university just got _____.

2. They _____ our account for the charge.

3. Jack was an _____ at the show.

4. Don is a _____ liar and cheat.

5. Our question _____ no response.

6. The _____ arrived in the mail.

7. The alarm _____ an ear-splitting shriek.

8. I never read an _____ in the paper.

9. The drought _____ the trees' growth.

10. We _____ the newsletter.

Spelling Lesson:

As you hear them, write the spelling words for the day in the space provided. Be sure that you correct any words you have spelled incorrectly.

1. _____

2. _____

3. _____

4. _____

5. _____

6. _____

7. _____

8. _____

9. _____

10. _____

11. _____

12. _____

13. _____

14. _____

15. _____

16. _____

17. _____

18. _____

19. _____

20. _____

21. _____

22. _____

23. _____

24. _____

25. _____

Using your words:

Choose at least ten words from your spelling list and use them in a short paragraph, silly story or poem.

Name_____ Date_____

Final Evaluation Test

Fill in the blanks with the missing letters.

1. If you can't take the heat, stay out of the k_____.

2. The doctor's s_____ was impossible to read.

3. I have a friend who works at a conve_____ store.

4. Did you pass your physical exam_____?

5. Make sure you take your med_____.

6. We spent hours scr_____ off the old wallpaper.

7. After we wr_____ all the presents, we added bows.

8. Did you get that cir_____ that advertises everything?

9. Did the dish and the spoon ever get m_____?

10. The ship was c_____ iron ore.

11. You would think that a capital would be in a c_____ location.

12. We made a dinner res_____.

13. Some of my best friends are highly cons_____.

14. We need some more inf_____.

15. I don't remember having that con_____.

16. A judge is supposed to be imp_____.

17. I love driving a con_____.

18. I'm not tired. I'm exh_____.

19. I enjoy all sports. I love comp_____.

20. You should l_____ up your muscles before exercising.

21. Do you really believe that this is unconstit_____?

22. I hope to con_____ something to mankind.

23. Not everybody can become w_____.

24. Does anybody like to hear sugg_____?

25. Have you ever met a fat diet_____?

Story Starters

Sometimes, pictures can inspire us to write poems or stories. Take a look
at the picture above. What do you think happened before and after? Has
something similar happened to you? How did you react? Think about these
questions as you write a short poem or story about this picture.

Story Starters

Sometimes, pictures can inspire us to write poems or stories. Take a look at the picture above. What do you think happened before and after? Has something similar happened to you? How did you react? Think about these questions as you write a short poem or story about this picture.

Story Starters

Sometimes, pictures can inspire us to write poems or stories. Take a look
at the picture above. What do you think happened before and after? Has
something similar happened to you? How did you react? Think about these
questions as you write a short poem or story about this picture.

Story Starters

Sometimes, pictures can inspire us to write poems or stories. Take a look at the picture above. What do you think happened before and after? Has something similar happened to you? How did you react? Think about these questions as you write a short poem or story about this picture.